NOT TODAY CANCER

Not Today Cancer

A NON-TYPICAL SURVIVAL GUIDE
FOR A GIRL WHO WANTS TO THRIVE,
NOT JUST SURVIVE

BY JEN DELVAUX

Charleston, SC
www.PalmettoPublishing.com

Not Today Cancer
Copyright © 2022 by Jen Delvaux

First Edition

Hardcover ISBN: 978-1-68515-612-1
Paperback ISBN: 978-1-68515-613-8
eBook ISBN: 978-1-68515-614-5

TO _____

FROM _____

To my husband Darren. Thank you for shining the light and leading the way. You are my superhero, my everything. To my children Maddie and Drew, my reasons to keep going and to never give up! I love you more…The end. I win!

To the incredible women I have met along this journey. I pray this book gives you the hope and courage you need. And to the millions of other women who will one day be touched by cancer. May this book help you take back your power.

Preface

The book you are about to embark on, which I have dreamt about writing for years (I just thought Darren was going to be the main character, not me), was able to come to fruition because of a leap of faith I took over 12 years ago. I was unhealthy, struggling with my weight, tired, lacking confidence and I knew I deserved more! I wanted more out of my life, so I started my own journey of getting healthy. I signed up as a Beachbody Coach, strictly for the discount, not having any intention of working the business. What happened though, was I lost weight, gained confidence, learned so much about my own health and was *happy* again. People took notice and started asking questions, so I slowly started working the business and learning everything I could about fitness, health and personal development. I wanted to help other women gain back their confidence and feel good again.

When Darren was diagnosed with brain cancer in 2009, I knew I had to step it up and not just treat this new venture as a side hustle. I wanted to be able to support my family with it, in case he couldn't go back to work. It didn't come easy, it took a lot of hard work, late nights and I had to overcome a lot of fears and self-doubt. In 2011 when his cancer returned, we were ready. He unfortunately couldn't go back to work after his second brain surgery, but thankfully the hard work had paid off.

I thank God every day that I looked past my fears and took that leap to do something more with my life. Because number one, I truly think it's how I was able to heal so quickly after my cancer diagnosis. I learned so much about health and fitness as a coach, so the changes I needed to make were super easy for me. Number two, I had the means to take the time off to heal and do all the extras that I discuss in this book. Lastly, leading a team and all the personal growth over the last 12 years gave me the confidence to write this book. Sometimes you need to do the things that scare you most to live the life you truly deserve!

You can get more information about my story at jendelvaux.com

You can also access any links, websites, podcasts, etc. that I discuss in this book at jendelvaux.com/bookresources.com.

TABLE OF CONTENTS

Introduction

What can start out as the scariest thing that could ever happen to you, may actually turn into something quite beautiful. Give it time. And put in the work.
—Jen Delvaux

I've never wanted to be called a survivor, although I know many people are proud of that word. I get it, but for me, I wanted more. I of course wanted to survive my diagnosis, but I wanted to *thrive* too! I wanted to learn from it, grow from it, and come out on the other side stronger, happier, and with a new passion for life. And that's exactly what I did. I'm not pretending it was all a bed of roses. This was the hardest thing I have ever endured, but today I can say I am in such a better place in my life than I was prior to my diagnosis. And I want this for you too.

That's why I'm so excited to invite you on this journey to take back your power. You feel so out of control when you hear the words "You have cancer." I celebrate you and challenge you to get grounded, grab a notebook right now, learn as much as you can, and commit to taking back your power and thriving after this crazy ride. Even when you don't feel that you have what it takes, I promise you that you are so much stronger than you think you are. I am not a doctor, nutritionist, or specialist, but I am a girl who has been through it all. My husband's brain cancer diagnosis and then my own breast cancer diagnosis have taught me so much. In fact, we joke around that I could perform brain surgery. I feel like an expert with all the research I have done. I'm here to guide you and share the things that I have learned.

In all my years of coaching driven and determined warriors just like you, I see the moments when you feel like you have nothing left to give. You feel powerless and hopeless. That is the breaking point. That's when you have to realize it's time to get going and discover how powerful you truly are and how the unexpected struggles of life can become your greatest strengths.

A diagnosis is scary. It's *so* important to protect your mind!

In her book *Unshakeable,* Christine Caine shares this:

One of the most important lessons I have discovered is that nothing is as powerful as a mind made up. It has the power to control the way your day—as well as your life—goes. We really don't have to think every train of thought that pops into our minds. Just like a real train, we can jump trains and even jump tracks. We don't have to let the train control where we go mentally and emotionally.

We have the power to control what we think. And consequently, we have the power to control who we become, because we are what we think, whether or not we choose to learn how to consciously control our thoughts. Learn to manage your mind, so your mind doesn't manage you. You have the power to jump tracks and change trains every time you need to. Consciously choose the trains that take you to God's precious and life-giving thoughts.

As you read through this book and hop on different trains of thought, pay attention to your destination.

On 2/22/21 (I'm a numbers girl; you'll see why in a bit) God *really* wanted to make it crystal clear that cancer was in my life for good. Maybe my purpose or calling, or whatever you want to call it, gave me a full understanding of my path in life. You see, my husband, Darren (we refer to him as Mr. Worldwide), was diagnosed with brain cancer in 2009. Three surgeries, *two* rounds of chemo (a year each), and two rounds of radiation later, now here we are dealing with the possibility of my own diagnosis of breast cancer?

The biopsy results came in on 2/22/21, with invasive ductal carcinoma, stage 1, grade 2 breast cancer…What the what? Really? How is this possible? Husband and wife *both* having cancer. I remember even when they called me back for a repeat mammogram, I kinda laughed it off. There's no way!

Even after they still saw it on my repeat mammogram, I thought, there's no way! Even after the ultrasound and they saw a lesion, I thought, there's no way! Unfortunately, I was wrong. Yes, it is possible for both husband and wife to have cancer.

I'm *extra* and over the top (just ask Mr. Worldwide), but if you simply implement just a few of the things you learn throughout this book, I know it will help you gain control over your diagnosis and give you a sense of peace. Your purpose behind the madness.

PART ONE:

Diagnosed with Breast Cancer—Now What?

Courage is being scared to death, but saddling up anyway.
—John Wayne

CHAPTER ONE:

Mindset and Belief

Get your mind right. Your happiness depends on it.
It's important to remember that everything is connected
between the mind and the body. You can eat all that
organic food and do all that yoga, but if you're angry
or stressed, much of the goodness goes to waste.
—*Kris Carr*

It's understandable that when you hear the words "You have cancer," you may go into total panic mode. My brain went to all the scariest possible outcomes, which is natural and okay. It's so very important to allow yourself to grieve. Allowing yourself time to vent your anger, frustration, and fears is just as important as staying positive. It's important to express *all* your emotions. It's interesting—Darren and I have handled our diagnosis *so* differently. For the most part, Darren has remained super positive. I joke around that they tweaked something during one of his brain surgeries for him to always be positive. I remember after my diagnosis when I was having a really hard time one day, he said, "But remember, this is a gift." I responded with, "No, I'm pissed! I don't want this." Do not beat yourself up when you are having a bad day. Allow all the feelings. Allow the tears, anger, and fears to move through you, but then you do need to make plans to turn it around.

A little story before I share some tips with you on mindset and belief:

A few months prior to my diagnosis, I kept seeing the number 11:11. Every day, multiple times throughout the day. The clock on the microwave, my coffee maker. Someone would send a message at

11:11 a.m., I would look at my phone at 11:11. It was constant. And to be honest, freaking me out a bit…like what does this mean? Was the universe trying to tell me something? I wasn't sure of the meaning, so I looked it up. It has several different meanings.

- It's a call to action, asking you to align your thoughts and actions with your highest good and best self.
- You are manifesting your thoughts, so keep them positive.
- Angels are trying to communicate. It's usually a message of importance. (This one made me wonder if it could possibly be my incredible stepmom, Leslie, who we lost to brain cancer in 2012, or my great-grandmother, who had been down this road before, sending me love and support from above.)
- A wake-up call that tells us to prepare for something greater to come. It's a time to manifest our intentions and take action to achieve our visions. Remember: thoughts are energy, and energy creates!

All of that resonated with me. Thinking back to the previous year, I was struggling a bit. I was going a million miles an hour but felt like I wasn't ever getting anywhere. I felt stuck, not sure where my life was going. I think I became a little short tempered as well. Little things were setting me off, which truly isn't typical for me. After learning the meaning of 11:11, I started to really slow down and pay attention to my thoughts and focus on what my intuition was telling me.

One day after seeing that number for the bajillionth time, I was like, "Okay God, angels above or the universe…What are you trying to tell me…" And suddenly, it popped into my head to schedule a mammogram. Weird, right?

Well, I trusted that thought and called right away. I was in fact past due, but only by a couple of weeks. That call to action was probably a lifesaver for me!

Throughout the process, I knew I was being guided and supported. When I see the number, I know I'm on the right path. Recently,
on Mother's Day, Darren gave me the most beautiful bracelet with
the number 11:11. The inside of the bracelet reads, "Remember who
you are." It's a reminder for me to slow down, pay attention to my
thoughts, forgive quickly, and know that I am being supported and
guided. That I can do hard things and come out even stronger.

Okay, back to the mindset and belief tips!

Here are some tips that have helped me:

1. Surround yourself with positive people and positive energy.
    I made a point to share with my friends and family that
    I didn't want *any* "poor Jenny" comments. I wanted only
    positivity. Even if they were talking with other people when
    I wasn't around. Nothing negative. I only wanted positive
    energy to flow. I shared that on social media as well. In fact,
    I even created my own cancer Facebook group for women,
    Stronger Together (You can join here: https://www.face-
    book.com/groups/nottodaycancer) OR go to the book re-
    source page at www.jendelvaux.com/bookresources. It is a
    positive, informative group to help women who have been
    diagnosed. There are many groups out there (I've been in
    them because of Darren) that were emotionally draining.
    So be careful when joining groups.

2. Change the way you look at things. The situation doesn't
    change, but you do. Find a way to shift your perspective so
    instead of seeing the glass half empty, you see it as half full.

    For example: When Darren and I go to appointments,
    we make a date out of it. Maybe we go for coffee before or
    lunch after. In fact, if we must travel for treatments, we turn
    it into a mini getaway and make some fun plans. Before

Darren's second surgery in Houston at MD Anderson, we had to be there several days early for testing. Instead of staying at one of the hospital hotels, we stayed in a swanky place, Hotel Zaza, which had a discounted hospital rate. Between appointments, we would lie poolside and enjoy a cocktail. We searched for some fun, delicious restaurants and truly lived it up. The night before his surgery, the Cowboys were playing (he's a die-hard Dallas Cowboy fan), so we rented one of the cabanas that were poolside to watch. The hotel was aware of his surgery and totally hooked us up. Remember—you earned that cancer card; use it when you need to. Try making the best out of this crazy situation you are in. Darren will also use his humor. If I say something about him having cancer, he always says, "I allegedly have cancer" with a little laugh.

3. Get a cancer crew. A positive crew, of course. Do not be in this alone. My girlfriend Jenelle knows that the second I start getting weepy or discouraged, she needs to set me straight.

She listens, of course, but because she knows me so well, she knows how to turn it around for me. I would also have another point person to look at all the things that maybe are pointless for you to know. I truly believe you do not need to know it all. Like all the possible side effects. Why put those in your head? Have a positive person who will make you laugh and take your mind off things when you have big appointments. Darren and I truly have had some of the best laughs and talks at our appointments. I remember after one of Darren's radiation appointments, we were in one of the changing rooms laughing so hard. The mask he had to wear for radiation was so tight on his face for some reason that it made him look like a lizard. People were actually looking at us like we were crazy when we walked out. But truly, laughter is the best medicine. You have to laugh at the crazy things that happen throughout your journey—there are going to be so many things that happen that may even shock you. You just have to shake your head and laugh. It makes the crazy situation easier, promise.

4. Name that negative voice in your head. This has helped me so much. Her name is Karen (my apologies to all the Karens out there), and I literally will tell her to F off! I know this may seem odd, but it does help. Or come up with a mantra. Some people with cancer have found that they can help turn their negative thoughts in a positive direction by repeating a mantra or phrase. Here are some of my favorite mantras I used during the tough days and some from my Instagram audience (thanks for sharing):
    - I am calm.
    - All is well.
    - I love where I am; I love where I'm going.
    - I can do hard things; I can endure anything for six months. (Erica)

- I surrender my worries to the universe.
- Not today mother f'er; not today. (Shelley)
- Wake, pray, slay. (Nicole)
- God's got this.
- My body knows exactly how to heal itself. (Sheri)
- I give myself permission to surrender to this experience completely because I know it's temporary. (Sheri)
- Every cell in my body is overflowing with health, healing, and love.
- My body heals quickly and easily.
- This, too, will pass.
- Everything I need to heal is already within me.
- Rocky Balboa the shit out of it (Malinda, huge Rocky fan)
- Keep moving forward. (Kate)

5. Keep a diary and write it all out. I can't even tell you how therapeutic and powerful it has been for me to get it all out on paper. The morning after I was diagnosed, I started writing and haven't stopped. Buy yourself a special and meaningful diary—one that you can't live without. More on this to come. (I dedicated an entire chapter to it.)

6. Prescription for fun. It's important to create fun during these difficult times.

   - Start every day with a smile and gratitude. Do this before you even get out of bed. Tell yourself something wonderful is going to happen today. And thank God for a new day.
   - Journal five things every morning that you are grateful for.
   - Monitor your media. Maybe turn off the depressing news for a bit. Or at least reduce it. Pay attention to the shows you're watching. A murder mystery or something that's disturbing won't boost your immune system—it can actually activate the stress response instead.
   - Watch more comedy that gets you laughing.
   - Hang with friends who lift you up and make you laugh. Laughter is a *huge* part of healing.
   - Get active: exercise, meditate, walk outside, dance, cook, give, take lessons, volunteer.
   - Create a joy list of fun things to do a few times a week and follow through with it.

NOT TODAY CANCER DAILY TIPS:

1. Eat mostly plants
2. Exercise
3. Prayer and meditation
4. Journal 5 things you are grateful for
5. Get 8 or more hours of sleep
6. 3 cups of green tea
7. Forgive others and yourself quickly
8. Choose to think positively
9. Laugh every day
10. Give your fears to God

CHAPTER TWO:

Your Super Calm—Meditation

In the midst of movement and chaos, keep stillness inside of you.
—Deepak Chopra

I had crippling fear when I was first diagnosed. I honestly didn't even think I would be able to drive myself to one of my early appointments. Remember, we were in COVID times, where you basically went to everything by yourself. I needed to do something, anything. I grabbed my phone and started searching for meditation apps. I found one, Unplug. There is a cost to this one, but there are free videos on YouTube as well. I'll share a few examples at the end of this chapter.

I would have paid just about anything at that point. I downloaded the Unplug app and searched the category "anxiety and stress" and found one called Superpower: CALM. It was lifesaving! No exaggeration. It was the first time since my diagnosis that I felt calm. This one nine-minute meditation gave me the tools I needed to remain calm for future appointments as well.

I continued to meditate daily from that day forward. Let me be very clear. I was terrible at mediation prior to this. I attempted this practice for years but could never quiet my mind and didn't have a full understanding of how truly powerful mediation can be. I don't think I ever made it three minutes prior to this! Now, it'll be with me every day of my life.

Mediation has so many amazing benefits for everyone. It has been found to decrease heart rate, lower blood pressure, ease muscle tension, and improve mood. Emotionally, the practice of meditation has helped many people restore a feeling of calm (which I desperately needed), by centering their thoughts and closing their minds to fears about the future. Meditation may also have specific benefits for people who are living with cancer. Some of these include:

Depression, anxiety, and stress. One study from UCLA, found a decrease in symptoms of depression for people with cancer after incorporating meditation. This was probably the biggest one for me. I have never dealt with depression, but definitely anxiety. After a meditation session on my mat, I always feel less anxious, and the worry and fear dissipate. These studies have found meditation to significantly improve the perception of stress. In fact, one study found that meditation decreased the levels of stress hormones in people with breast and prostate cancer and that the effects were still present a year later. That's how powerful it is! Meditation may also lower the levels of Th1 cytokines, which are inflammatory factors produced by the body that may affect how we respond to cancer and our healing from cancer.

Sleep problems. Difficulty with sleep is a common problem for people living with cancer. Lordy, this has been one of my top issues because of those lovely medically induced menopause symptoms. In studies, meditation is associated with less insomnia and improved quality of sleep. Plus, with the breathing techniques I've learned from meditating, I fall back to sleep faster after a hot flash.

Cognitive functioning. Difficulty with cognitive functioning is common and may be due to the cancer itself or treatments for cancer, such as chemotherapy (chemo brain is real). The studies from UCLA found meditation to improve cognitive functioning with cancer. I think it's because it teaches us so much about slowing down, being present and calm.

Fatigue. Weirdly, you would think that meditating would make you sleepy, right? But I feel so energized after. Can we all agree cancer fatigue is one of the most annoying symptoms when dealing with treatment and just having cancer? When I was going through radiation, it reminded me of that first trimester of pregnancy, where you could just fall asleep anywhere. That was me with radiation, but everyone is different. Studies from UCLA suggest that meditation may improve energy levels and lessen fatigue for people living with cancer.

Now that you understand the benefits, it's time to get started.

How to meditate and incorporate it into your already busy schedule:

- Baby steps. I used to think you had to meditate for hours for it to truly work. Nope. I typically only do ten minutes a day. If that seems like too much, start with five minutes a day. Make it work for you. There have been days when I needed more because of my anxiety, but now that I'm through the tough stuff, ten minutes works perfectly.
- Realize there is no right way or wrong way to meditate. I don't think it worked for me previously because I honestly didn't think I was doing it right, so I stopped. I thought it was a waste of time. It's not! Trust me. It's going to take a bit to get used to, like anything does. The hardest part is quieting our busy minds. Even today when I'm meditating, I still have to direct my wandering brain back to my breath. I also thought you had to be sitting in a particular position. You do not. Some of my best meditations were when I was lying down or walking on the beach.
- You don't have to do it alone: I love guided meditations. If you are new to meditation like I was (I feel like I still am), guided meditations are a great place to start. They're like a cheat sheet for how to be calm. Like I mentioned earlier, I'm a huge fan of the app Unplug. It has a ton of guided meditations for whatever you need in your life. Sleep, anxiety and stress, happiness and positivity, mindfulness,

sound healing (I'm obsessed with sound baths—A Sound Bath is a deeply immersive, full-body listening experience that intentionally uses sound to invite gentle yet powerful therapeutic and restorative processes to nurture your mind and body.) Unplug does have a cost to it, but it is so worth it! Or you can search on YouTube for a free version (I share a few below). There are various podcasts that post daily guided meditations to try out as well.

Here are a few different meditation podcasts you can check out. Search these within your podcast app:

- Guided Meditation
- The Daily Meditation Podcast
- Mindful in Minutes

Know this: You can't do this wrong. If you are attempting to meditate daily, you are doing it right. There's really no way to mess this up. Promise. Actually, I take that back. You can mess it up if you aren't doing it. You will have great mediations, and maybe ones where you are a little more distracted. That's A-okay. Just keep at it daily. Your body and mind will thank you.

Here are a few free meditations I mentioned earlier in this chapter: (Reminder you can access all links and suggestions at www.jendelvaux. com/bookresources).

- https://youtu.be/ZToicYcHIOU
- https://youtu.be/W19PdslW7iw
- https://youtu.be/86m4RC_ADEY

CHAPTER THREE:

Talking with the Kids

> *Anything that is human is mentionable and anything that*
> *is mentionable can be more manageable. When we can*
> *talk about our feelings, they become less overwhelming,*
> *less upsetting and less scary. The people we trust with that*
> *important talk can help us know that we are not alone.*
> —*Fred Rogers*

Share your diagnosis with your kids openly and honestly, but I do think it's important for you to be in the right headspace. Where you can explain it calmly and eliminate as many fears as possible for the kids. I'm not saying you need to fake it and pretend this is not a big deal, because it *is* a big deal. I just wouldn't share all the details—at least not yet.

Kids can typically take it straight up. They're going to hear this word a lot, so make them very familiar with it. If your diagnosis is a complex word, break it down for them so that the scary unknown is brought into the light.

We didn't have any sort of guidance on how to do this, so it's not like we did everything 100 percent right. We listened to our hearts and did our best. This little bit said, I do think there are a couple of things to pay attention to when you have this discussion with your kids.

Talking Tip #1: Recognize your kids as individuals
"Find your thing that comforts you, maybe a certain place or activity."—Drew Delvaux (our 16 year old son)

This includes respecting their feelings. Any parent with two or more kids knows this: your kids are different from each other. It is also not one size fits all in communication style with each of them.

They're going to handle the struggle, or whatever it is you're going through, differently.

Maddie and Drew were opposites. Drew was four when Darren was first diagnosed, and Maddie was nine. Both were in grade school, and each handled the situation very differently.

Drew asked a lot of questions and wanted to be involved. Maddie was very quiet, but I could see in her eyes that her mind was going nonstop. She dealt with it internally, where Drew wanted to be very hands on.

I think it's important to have kids talk to a professional. Maddie always did. I think for some kids there may be a stigma going to therapy, like it's a thing that they have to do because they have a problem. I think therapy is one of the most helpful things you can do for yourself when dealing with a cancer diagnosis.

But Drew hated it. We asked him, "Drew, what do you think about all this stuff?"

Drew said, "I don't know. I just think about it to myself."

We said, "Do you talk to anybody about it? Do you have friends that you talk to?"

We did try to get him into therapy, and I went with him. He was so uncomfortable. He refused and never wanted to go back. He wasn't open to it yet.

Now, since he is sixteen years old and this cancer issue is still with us, Drew does talk to us a lot, but still says, "I just talk to myself or my friends."

As parents, that can be worrisome, because we know this family health issue is a traumatic event that is going to come out in some sort of way. So I'm hoping Drew has a "monkey see, monkey do" response to Darren and me—we love therapy, so maybe he'll give it a try again.

Maddie is now twenty-two and loves it and recognizes how much it's helping her.

So recognize that your children are individuals, and tailor how you talk to them and get them the support they need, because each one is going to be different.

They won't have your feelings or reactions. In fact, they may not have each other's, either. You shouldn't be expecting your child to have the same emotions as you—or as his sibling(s). A family is full of in-dividuals—unique, with different sets of emotional perspectives. Each kid processes things differently. Respect their feelings.

Talking Tip #2: Be open and honest with your children

"Positivity worked for our family, joking about it…Talking and being honest" ~ Maddie Delvaux (our 22 year old daughter)

One of the times when Darren had a seizure, we were at home; we had the whole family over for dinner. The kids happened to be upstairs playing basketball. My cousin called 911, and an ambulance came. My family was like, "Jen, just go now," because we were leaving in an am-bulance, and they were trying to keep it a secret from the younger kids.

I said, "No, no, no. We have to tell Drew. Drew will know and worry if suddenly we were gone from this dinner." So, I said to him, "Hey, listen, Drew. it's going to be okay. Dad and I are going to the hospital, and I'll call you in a little bit."

He became a little panicked, but he appreciated the honesty. He was relieved to be included. He told us that later. We knew that about him.

If you don't use the word "cancer" (and in our case "brain cancer," "breast cancer," etc.), they will get confused about your illness. They may think that you're just dealing with the flu or a cold they could po-tentially catch. *Cancer* is a very powerful word that will stop people in their tracks. When you're talking to a child, use the word *cancer* openly, but never be nonchalant about it. Never be dismissive of the treatments your diagnosis calls for.

Keeping your diagnosis a secret could actually cause higher anxiety levels in children who are not informed of the parent's condition. Kids can sense when something is wrong. If they hear you whispering or overhear a phone conversation with a doctor, they may even worry that it's something worse. Trust me, rather than keeping your diagnosis a secret, take this as an opportunity to have life-changing discussions with your kids. Make them gentle teaching moments.

When my mom was a young child, her grandmother was diagnosed with breast cancer. People whispered about her diagnosis, making my mom more fearful of what was going to happen to her grandmother.

"I was about eight when my fifty-year-old grandmother was diagnosed with breast cancer. She had a radical mastectomy on one side only. I heard my parents whispering and heard the word *cancer*. I didn't really know what that was, but I knew it was bad because my mom was crying. No one talked about cancer, it was like a curse. I was afraid when I did see my grandmother, but you know what? She was doing just great! She lived to be eighty-four, with a little blip of a repeat cancer diagnosis when she was seventy-nine. She said, 'This is an insult!' after she had the other breast removed. She was a true cancer warrior, before her time. Her death was not cancer related."

Thankfully, kids are not kept in the dark these days. With all the information on the internet and social media, parents should be more proactive in their discussions with their children. How terrible would it be if your kids found out about it on Facebook? Adults may talk as well, and you surely don't want them to hear it from their friends. Or if they just decided to google it on their own. There is a ton of misinformation on the internet. I made sure to explain this to my kids. You can't believe everything you read. That goes for the patient as well.

Trying to act like this is no big deal will not do them any favors either. Again, you don't need to be nonchalant or dismissive about it;

just be as honest as you can without scaring them. I know it's easier said than done, but I can tell you this: We are so close with our kids because we have been open and honest about almost everything. We didn't share with them that the doctor only gave Darren eighteen months to live (twelve years ago). And thank God we didn't, because as you can see, that doctor was very wrong. But I do think you can prepare them for how your treatment may affect you and them.

Remember, always lead with your heart. You know your kids better than anyone. You can listen to a recent episode from our podcast show, Not Today Cancer (episode number 149), where our kids share their perspectives on having parents with cancer.

Or go to the book resource page at jendelvaux.com/bookresources.

PART TWO:

Navigating the Diagnosis

*You are allowed to scream, you are allowed
to cry, but do not give up.*
—Unknown

CHAPTER FOUR:

Funnel Your Feelings—Journaling

The entire universe is conspiring to give
you everything that you want.
—Abraham Hicks

That's been my jam through this entire journey. It has helped me process my feelings and kept me sane. I thought it may be helpful to share my first couple of journal entries. The few nights after I found out I had cancer, I would be up in the middle of the night consumed with fear. I would wake up at the crack of dawn and start journaling. Getting those emotions/feelings out was so therapeutic for me. Let me share some of my early journal entries to give you an idea of how I organized my thoughts.

2/13/21

I received a call that I needed to do a repeat mammogram and ultrasound, but I wasn't worried. I thought there's no way this can be anything, but one weird thing the nurse on the phone asked was "Do you want to know which breast it is?" I was like, "sure," but before she could even tell me, in my head I was saying it's my left, my left, she's going to say left. Yes, sure enough, she said, "it's your left breast." I have no idea how I knew that, but I did! I've never felt a lump or anything, but I still wasn't worried.

2/18/21

During the repeat mammogram in the first two pictures, she couldn't find anything. Sweet! But there it was on the third picture. She said, "Let me have the radiologist take a look, and then we'll know if he wants you to move forward with the ultrasound." Yup, we were moving forward with the ultrasound.

While I was waiting to go back, I took a picture and shared a poll on my Instagram stories asking the percentage of people who had to get repeat mammograms. *So* many people came back to me saying this was normal. Even nurses. This calmed me.

Once in the ultrasound room, my fears started creeping in. The technician had a serious look on her face and wasn't saying much. I could see concern on her face, and she stayed in one area for a long time. After what seemed like an eternity, she said, "I'm going to have the doctor come back and go over the results with you."

Shit! I knew that was not good! They told me early on that you don't see the doctor unless they see something. My stomach was in knots.

The nicest yet seriously concerned doctor came in, and I just could tell by the look on his face that it wasn't good. He said, "I'm surprised you haven't felt anything on your left breast. We are definitely seeing a lesion 9mm by 13mm. I'm thinking there is a chance this could be cancer."

But in my mind, I kept thinking there was no way. Husband and wife both can't have cancer, right? He asked me if I had any questions, I was like, "No, I'm good thank you." I just wanted to get out of there as soon as I could to get home to Darren and Drew. Remember, I was alone because of COVID. They said someone would be contacting me within the next day or two to schedule a biopsy.

I was a little more nervous on the ride home, but not terribly. No tears, just hope that this was still nothing. Literally, my sister and mom had just gone through this, and it ended up being nothing a month prior.

I talked with my neighbor who had just gone through this as well. She was like, "The good news is they didn't take you right back then and there and do the biopsy."

I was like, "Ohhhhhh, okay, yes!" Again, that made me feel better.

Minutes later, my phone rang.

I think it had only been twenty minutes since I'd arrived home from the appointment. It was the nurse going over the biopsy and what to expect. She said, "The doctor spent quite some time looking everything over, and he is pretty sure this is cancer, so we need you back tomorrow morning for the biopsy."

What?

Now full-on panic set in. I'm a very strong person. I can handle most anything, but I was a mess. I could *not* hold it together. The wine that Darren served me might have brought on more tears, but I needed it. I was trying to hold it together for Drew (my fifteen-year-old son at the time) when he would come down, but there was no hiding it. No lashes, swollen and puffy bloodshot eyes. Drew is not your typical teenager; he is an old soul. He was so calming, talking to me about other things…just so sweet. I also messaged Maddie (my twenty-one-year-old daughter at the time). Her response was "You're gonna be okay, Mama. We've been through it all, and we can handle anything. Love you more than anyone. You are a strong woman. You Know that." That was what I needed to hear.

We went to sleep that night—well, I pretended I was. I just laid there all night. When I got up the next day, I was like, "I got this! Get it together. I can do this." If you follow me on social media, you know my morning routine is everything. I made my coffee, listened to affirmations, and started journaling. I started to feel calm again.

This is why I recommend journaling. Once you get it out of your head, you can work through it all so much better. It brings you a sense of peace. I didn't know what would ever come of it. I just knew that it was helping me to get out of all my emotions. I now thank God I did, because we forget things over time. I refer to it often now so I can be a light for other women going through it. As I was sharing this part of my journal, I was thinking I may share it all one day. It truly captures every moment.

Let's dive into some of the scientific research and the benefits of journaling when dealing with a diagnosis. For many people, keeping a journal is an easy way to express their feelings and document their journey. I truly believe (because, hello, I've lived it), writing about something as stressful and difficult as cancer can be so healing. In fact, there is scientific research showing that expressing your innermost thoughts and feelings can reduce stress and promote a range of other physical, emotional, and social benefits.

Early research from American Society of Clinical Oncology into the benefits of expressive writing for people with cancer, found women with breast cancer who wrote about their deepest thoughts and feelings reported the fewest symptoms and had the fewest unscheduled visits to their doctors. I find that so interesting!

You don't have to be a good writer. You don't even have to share it, but getting those emotions and feelings out is *so* powerful for your well-being.

How to Get Started with Journaling:

1. Did you order your journal yet? Get your favorite pens? I love gel pens…of course, the pink ones. Pen and paper are best, but you can always use your computer as well. I'm usually a pen-to-paper girl, unless I am writing in my cancer chronicles journal on my computer. Whichever you choose, set a realistic goal and have fun with it. Maybe five minutes in the mornings. Or on the weekends. Make it work for you.

2. Journaling in the morning is best. Grab a cup of coffee or tea (more on tea later) and start writing. In my opinion, the best time to write is in the morning because typically it is when your mind is most quiet and free from external influences. Although it is really dependent on your personality and whether you are an early riser or a night owl. I'm an early riser. I set my alarm an hour before anyone else because I know how important this is.

3. If you are stumped on what to journal about, you can always use prompts. There are many journals out there that prompt you. If I'm not writing in my cancer chronicles on my computer, I use my push journal (you can access in the book resources page at jendelvaux.com/bookresources).

This journal prompts me to write what I'm grateful for. I use the notes section on the back to write out my affirmations. Then I plan out my day.

If journaling and writing out paragraphs makes you feel intimidated, you could always write out lists instead. For example:

- Things you feel good about.
- Things that you are concerned about and how you can let that go or work through it.
- Dreams you have for your life.
- Where you see yourself in five years. Have fun with this. Get excited.
- The things you want to get done that day.
- All the things you are grateful for.

Just like with meditation, you can't do this wrong. In fact, it can truly improve your life. I write down my affirmations daily in the present tense as if they were already happening. I feel it, I see it, and get excited. Recently I went through one of my old journals and was *so* amazed at all the things I had manifested into my life.

- I wanted to hit a certain level in my business. I exceeded it
- I wanted to take my family on a trip to Hawaii. Darren used to laugh this off and say, "There's no way we could afford that." We went twice.
- I wanted to be part of the cast in a TurboFire video (any TurboFire fans out there?). It was one of the highlights of my life. To be on that set was such a cool experience. I just couldn't walk for days after. Haha!
- I wanted to write a book. Ahhhhh…I'm doing it now.

These are just a few of my examples—just by simply grabbing a pen and paper and writing it out.

Roxy the Radiator and my Team at Lacks Cancer Center

CHAPTER FIVE:
Treatment—It's No Longer One Size Fits All

*Cancer is messy and scary. You throw everything
at it, but don't forget to throw love at it. It turns
out that might be the best weapon of all.*
—Unknown

Some start with surgery, others start with chemo. Some only do surgery and nothing else. Some do a unilateral mastectomy, while some do a bilateral mastectomy. Some do it all, and some choose to heal themselves. It's so dependent on your stage, grade, doctors, and what *you* choose to do. I thought it would be helpful to share some stories from myself and other women and the specific treatments we all went through.

I'll start. The treatment I had was a lumpectomy, injections to shut down my ovaries, radiation, and hormone-blocking meds.

You know the story of my diagnosis, but you may not know the treatments I had.

I started with a lumpectomy to remove the tumor. The surgery went really well. She got clear margins, and they only found one cancer cell in my lymph node, which they said is considered negative. The Oncotype score did come back a little higher than we had hoped (21), so for a bit there, we thought chemo might be on the table. But after a couple of weeks of going over things and getting some things retested, we decided to not do chemo. I did radiation, followed by Zoladex injections (to shut down my ovaries), and hormone-blocking meds. To eliminate the monthly Zoladex injections, I eventually opted to have my ovaries removed. Of course, all this blasted me into menopause.

I want to share my radiation experience with you, so you are prepared for what to expect.

It doesn't matter how much meditation or prayer you do, that first time is scary. I changed out of my clothes and into my robe and sat in the lounge area. Kinda feels like you are going to the spa, but you are not...unfortunately. When the technician came to get me, I felt like I was having an out-of-body experience—like I was watching myself. It's so weird walking down that hallway the first time. I walked into the room, and when I saw my machine had eyes, eyelashes, and a little bow, it made me feel *so* much better. I actually named the radiation machine, "Roxy the Radiator".

I got on the table, and as they were positioning me, I started praying. A tip that one of my friends from Instagram gave me was to pick someone each day to pray for. And even let that friend know. It truly helps so much because it takes it off you! Plus, by telling that person, they will hopefully be thinking and praying for you as you are going through it.

Okay, so the positioning takes a bit of time. In fact, it's probably longer than the actual radiation. Once they feel like the tattoos are matched up (yes, you get little dot tattoos, but honestly, I can barely see mine), then they do an x-ray to make sure everything is aligned.

Then they leave the room and treatment begins. If you have left-sided breast cancer like me, you have to hold your breath during treatment, so it elongates your heart to get it out of the way of the beam. I was worried about this, but no worries, If you start breathing, the machine stops. I practiced at home before I went in, which made me more comfortable. I would time myself to see how long I could hold my breath. Then I would focus on counting while it was going. I also pictured any cancer cells popping during the treatment. I think holding your breath actually helps to distract yourself during the treatment. And it's fast—maybe like five minutes.

I felt badass after that first treatment. I felt *so* powerful. I was so scared prior to it, and as you go through these scary things, you are going to realize how strong you truly are.

The first day after radiation my left breast was swollen and warm to the touch. This isn't typical, but weird things do happen. I think my breast was angry, like, what are you doing? But that went away the next day.

In the middle of radiation treatments fatigue was definitely setting in. Again, everyone is different, so you may not experience this.

I fell into such a routine. I fully knew what was going to happen:

1. I would get on the table, and they would position me by moving the blanket. They wanted me to lie super still, heavy body, with my arms above my head, holding handles. As they were doing this, I was praying for someone.
2. They would take pictures to make sure everything was lined up and then leave the room.
3. When Roxy the Radiator was positioned and I heard the buzzing sound, I knew it was "go time."
4. I would work on my breathing and pray that God's hands were on me protecting my other organs. And I would picture the cancer cells popping.

It's so important to have positive thoughts about what you are doing. Instead of looking at all the negative things that can happen from it, look at how it's going to get rid of the cancer and heal you.

During treatment, your body uses a lot of energy dealing with the effects of radiation on normal cells. It usually builds up slowly during the course of treatment, particularly toward the end, and it may last for some weeks or months after treatment finishes. Many people find that they cannot do as much as they normally would, but others are able to continue their usual activities.

Remember, everyone is going to handle this differently. Some people get through this so easily, and some feel the exhaustion more quickly. Honestly, I thought I would power through it, but I didn't. Everyone has their own unique experience with it.

Give yourself grace. Rest when you need it. You are helping your body to heal. And it needs it right now. When you have energy, get the important things done. Just make sure you are taking some things off your plate.

And now stories from other thrivers.

Katy Weade. IG @katyweade. Life and parenting coach. Treatment: chemo, bilateral mastectomy, and radiation.

In April 2021, I was diagnosed with breast cancer at the age of forty-one. The most shocking part of my diagnosis is that I had a "normal" mammogram with no cancer detection in February of the same year. The reason I went back in after the normal mammogram was because I had a small lump in my left breast and a cyst in the right breast that had gotten bigger, neither of which raised red flags on the mammogram. I knew I had dense breast tissue and was concerned that because of that, they might have missed something. Sure enough, my gut instinct was spot on. It turned out that the left breast had a benign lump, but I had cancer in my right breast and lymph nodes. I had no family history or major risk factors, so it was suggested in my report that I "may" benefit from further testing such as ultrasound. I firmly believe that women with dense breasts should have mandatory additional screening. Dense breast tissue shows up white on a mammogram; so does cancer. Not following up to sift out what was dense tissue vs. actual cancer would have cost me my life. Bottom line: Dense breasts need more tests.

My diagnosis was invasive ductal carcinoma, ER+ PR+ HER2- with a very aggressive grade 3 tumor that had spread to my lymph nodes extensively. Although 100 percent estrogen fueled, my cancer was mimicking triple negative. Because of this specific diagnosis, it was recommended that we do chemotherapy first, then surgery, then radiation. I endured sixteen rounds of chemo (Adriamycin [the "Red Devil"] + Taxol) and had a double mastectomy with immediate reconstruction.

I am happy to report that I had a full response to chemotherapy and surgery and was recently declared cancer free. It was a whirlwind of a year, but I'm coming out stronger on the other end. I have been asked a lot how I got through all this with such a positive attitude and seemingly minimal side effects, and my answer to that is simple—go back to the basics. Slow down, listen to your body, and take care of yourself mentally and physically. I cleaned up my diet, hydrated like crazy, stayed active, found a life coach who had the mindset I wanted to embody, released my fears, let my friends and family in, accepted help, and held my head high. I cried when I needed to, focused on my kids, and took it one day at a time.

My motto has been to be even better after breast cancer. I'll do that by continuing to advocate for myself and sticking to the basics for living a happy, healthy life. My journey can be found on my Instagram highlights (@katyweade).

Paula Maier. IG @paulashealthyliving. Breast cancer warrior. Treatment: chemo, unilateral mastectomy, and radiation.

In June 2020 I was diagnosed with triple negative lobular breast cancer.

I began my journey with four sessions of the Red Devil (AC), and twelve sessions of Taxol and Carbo.

January 21, 2021, I had a bilateral mastectomy.

Having a mastectomy vs. a lumpectomy was not negotiable. My cancer mass was 6cm. That's the size of a small lime. It was in all four quadrants of my breast. The surgeon also removed ten lymph nodes and some armpit tissue. There were cancer cells in two of the nodes.

Because of COVID, my husband could come to the hospital and be with me before surgery, but only one hour after surgery. Until discharge, I was on my own.

I woke up and was determined to start my hallway walks with my IV stand. I had no pain in my chest due to the pain-blocking meds. On the hour, I would make my way down the hallways and keep up with drinking water to flush the anesthesia out of my system. The nurses joked that I was like Mario Andretti. I had a drain coming out of the side, which had to be emptied and measured. I had full mobility before I left the hospital. I attribute that to lifting weights four or five times a week for many years prior to my diagnosis, and all through chemotherapy. When I got home and the pain block wore off, the discomfort was manageable, so I chose not to take pain meds other than Tylenol. By day three I took one pain pill, but it didn't really affect the way I felt. Dealing with the drain and not lifting anything over five pounds was a challenge. But I followed the directions. On day four, my surgeon said I could get on my stationary bike and do an easy spin. It empowered me in my recovery to get back to my workout room.

I had the drain in several days past what was typical, but I had had this same issue years earlier, so that is just the way I ride. After two weeks, when the lifting restrictions were lifted, I began my weight lifting with super-light weights, just going through the motions. I walked my dogs out on the street as the weather allowed.

After being approved by the surgeon, I began basic PT (physical therapy) stretches. I made an appointment with a physical therapist to learn more exercises, and three weeks post-surgery I rebegan my massage appointments. My therapist had experience dealing with women who had mastectomies, and I felt very safe with the process. I did this intent on not losing mobility and keeping lymphedema and cording at bay.

I had some cording, but weekly massage and eight sessions of PT relieved it.

I also had a compression garment ordered for my arm and hand, which I will have to wear every time I fly for life.

If you ask me how I deal with having a DD breast and being completely flat on the other side, it depends on the day. I have a prosthetic that I use when I go to the gym or am dressing up for the evening. When I'm at home, or walking in my neighborhood, I don't use a prosthetic. I take pictures for my business Instagram page (PaulasHealthyLiving), and I often don't wear it. It can annoy my skin (a month after my mastectomy, I did twenty-five sessions of radiation with a bolus bonus because of the size of the tumor) because radiation continues to be changing my skin and tissue to this day.

I have up days and troubling days just like everyone, but my determination, drinking sixty-four-plus ounces of unsweetened tea or water every day, eating clean unprocessed foods, and regular exercise have helped me retain my mobility and strength.

I'm thankful for all the medical advances that are available to me to fight and beat cancer!

Update on Paula! She just had an MRI the week of 12/23/21, and it showed both sides are cancer free!

Kelly Barton. IG @kc_barton. Breast cancer thriver. Treatment: chemo and bilateral mastectomy.

I was diagnosed with triple positive (estrogen, progesterone, and HER2 positive) invasive ductal carcinoma breast cancer in January 2018 after finding a lump in my breast. At the time of my diagnosis, I was an avid runner and took my health very seriously. I remember feeling betrayed by my body and like I had no control over what was happening.

I had a port inserted and a lymph node dissection done soon after. And soon after that, I started chemo. A few days after my second round of chemo, my hair started coming out by the handful, so my girlfriends went with me to have my head shaved. As much as I told myself it was just hair, this was pretty traumatic.

One of the things that helped me through the roughest days of chemo was exercise. I made a point of getting outside every day. Sometimes it was only to walk a block or two, and sometimes I went for a run with friends. I also tried to give myself as much grace as possible. If I was only up for walking a block, that was OK. And I allowed friends and family to help me with meals, shopping, and cleaning.

When I was getting close to my sixth and final round of chemo, I was on a walk with a friend, and we were talking about how I wanted to celebrate this milestone. She said, "You have always wanted to plan a 5k. You should do that!"

What started as a crazy idea between friends became My Breast Friends 5k and Silent Auction. Since 2018 we have raised over $60,000 for local cancer patients through Oregon Cancer Foundation.

On June 28 I had a bilateral mastectomy with reconstruction. My surgeon had only recommended a unilateral mastectomy, but my feeling was that my cancer was aggressive, so I was going to fight it in the most aggressive way possible. The recovery was not easy, but I know the decision was the right one for me.

When my husband and I came home on January 8, 2018, after receiving my cancer diagnosis, I told him, "Something good will come from this." I don't think you have to do something as big as planning a 5k but focusing my attention on how I could help others helped me in more ways than I can express.

Sae Jackson. IG @sunnysae. Treatment: bilateral mastectomy.

My diagnosis came on October 27, 2021. I saw a picture of the kids wearing pink at my kids' boarding school for breast cancer awareness. I couldn't remember when I last did a self-exam, I found the lump doing a self-exam. I have very dense breasts with many cysts and thought it was just another cyst. We currently live in Saudi Arabia as expats, and I was just thinking about going to get a mammogram when

I'm home this summer. My husband pushed the issue for me to make an appointment with the doctor and see what she said.

We have John Hopkins on our compound. When I did a video conference with the doctor, she immediately booked me for a mammogram. When I went, they couldn't get a good image, so they did an ultrasound. A few days later, I saw my reading come up on our app that it could be possible malignancy, and a biopsy was recommended to get a better insight. I cried in my GP's office, and she said, "Don't worry until you have to worry." Eighty percent of the time, she saw these reports come back as being noncancerous after the biopsy.

A week later I had my biopsy, and when I turned to see the ultrasound as the doctor was doing the biopsy, I knew it was cancer. The shape, borders—it wasn't like the cyst I saw on the ultrasound.

A few days later, on October 27, I received my diagnosis. Immediately my GP assured me she would be following my case and what all the steps were. I was immediately given an oncology nurse to contact. Judith, my oncology nurse, had been my angel through all this. She handpicked all my doctors, and they were all amazing for me. Any questions, concerns, or emergencies I have had, she has been there. I have her direct phone line and can text her, and she responds immediately.

I started my research. Being a nurse, I knew how to research evidence-based practice. I decided on a bilateral mastectomy. I didn't want to live my life wondering if this cancer would come back with a vengeance.

I told my oncology surgeon, plastics, and oncologist my decision. They all gave me the facts that a total mastectomy wasn't needed and why but left it up to me to decide. They even had me meet with a surgeon, not on my team, to give me information. Mostly they were making sure I had the facts and was comfortable with a double mastectomy. They wanted me to know I was able to change my mind anytime leading up to my surgery.

On November 21, 2021, I had a bilateral mastectomy. I stayed in the hospital for thirty-six hours. I had no pain after thirty-six hours, was able to go home pain free, and had use of my arms with no issues. I had a skin-sparing total mastectomy (nipples removed as well), with expanders put in preparing for implants.

My cancer was contained to the tumor; nothing was spread into my nodes. I am estrogen and progesterone positive, HER2 negative, and currently waiting for my Oncotype test to come back. At this time the oncologist believes I only need Tamoxifen. They also did a cancer genetic test, and all came back negative for any breast and gynecological cancer, which is a big relief for me since I have a daughter.

I just finished my last expansion of 350cc yesterday, and now I will see plastics, mostly to monitor, and we are hoping for implants surgery in approximately three months.

Tina Wienecke. IG @funnerhealthnut. Integrative health coach. Treatment: holistic approach.

I did not have a traditional diagnosis. In early 2018, I was assured by two radiologists, even after receiving negative pathology reports, that what they could see on imaging was cancer but that their job was not to diagnose. They requested that I see an oncological breast surgeon. Before seeing the surgeon, I contacted a best friend's husband who is a pathologist and is co-owner of a pathology lab. He told me that unfortunately, even though pathology is the one to give the true diagnosis, in over 50 percent of cases in which radiology disagrees due to what they see on their screen, radiology is correct because cells could have been missed during biopsies, and the lab is only seeing a sliver of cells, which is not the full picture.

While this was discouraging, I opted to move forward in visiting with a surgeon in the Houston Medical Center. I traveled down with my husband and sister-in-law along for support, and they endured the entire appointment with me. I was adamant that the surgeon explain the images I brought her on disk—their shapes, their meaning, and why she would or would not concur with radiology. She was insistent that the left side imaging was consistent with typical breast cancer that she saw daily. Her exact words were "this is textbook cancer." She recommended operating within four weeks, with the caveat that she could not guarantee that the operation would be the end of the cancer. It could require more surgery, chemo, and/or radiation. I never returned.

Within three days I had made the decision to fight on my own. I sought the expertise of an epigeneticist, who collaborated with me to help equip my body with appropriate nutrients so my body could do what it is designed to—heal itself. In addition, though I thought I was living a clean life, I did a radical 180 in lifestyle that included nutrition, exercise, detoxification, stress reduction, and so on. While I was not overweight, a side effect was losing eighteen pounds, which I have kept off with ease. By September 2018, there were no signs of cancer, and ultrasounds were clear. It has been almost four years since I began reversal, and I am still cancer free. I continue to practice a disease-free lifestyle because I know the benefits of living it.

From April to September of 2018, my feet hit the floor every single morning with a little fear, but mostly optimism that I would do whatever I needed to that day to win. I faced each day one at a time and stayed the course. I had an amazing support system, and I became bold enough to remove myself from relationships that did not serve me well. Along with cleaning up my dietary intake and being extremely picky about it, I increased acupuncture, exercised a lot more, and added more variety, stimulated lymphatic drainage, laughed and made jokes to my immediate family about my condition (I needed levity), and most of all, I learned to tap into my very strong intuition, which meant listening to my body and giving it half a chance to demonstrate its power.

Losing your hair. It's me again. For a couple of weeks, I thought I would be having chemo. Several doctors recommended this based on my Oncotype score. I feel like this was the hardest thing for me to accept. I felt like I was losing my identity. I didn't want to be that "sick" person and have everyone looking at me with such sadness. I'm a strong person and didn't want people to worry and feel sorry for me. I thought I was being so vain and ridiculous, but after talking to so many women, I realized I wasn't alone. After a good cry and some sleep, I pulled myself together and started searching for wigs... *dang*...wigs are expensive! I had no idea. But again, with me being extra and all, I knew this would be important for me. But I didn't end up going the chemo route. My oncologist felt comfortable with not doing chemo after recalculating my Oncotype score with no lymph node involvement. Originally, they had calculated it with having lymph node involvement, but it was only one node. My doctor said that's actually considered no node involvement. So no chemo for me. The final decision was ultimately mine, looking at the percentages and knowing I would be making drastic changes with my healing, I felt comfortable going this route. But so many women do have to go through this, so I wanted to share a story from one of my breasties, Holly Boyce.

Holly Boyce. IG @thehollyboyce. The confidence queen and twelve-year breast cancer thriver.

RIP to my hair.

"Bald is the new blonde" and "Does this shirt make my head look bald?" were some of the common shirts I wore during my six-month chemo treatments. It was great making so many people laugh when I walked into the chemo room each week. I loved being the one who was making them smile. I tried really hard to stay positive and keep people laughing, but some days it was not easy.

I loved my long blond hair (or whatever highlighted version of it that it was then). I had long hair my whole life. It was who I was. It was what defined me. Losing hair during treatment was the last thing I wanted. What amazes me still is that I considered not doing the treatments that the doctor recommended because I didn't want to be bald. I remember thinking I was so shallow for thinking that, but it was more than that. It was more the admission to the world that I was now a cancer patient. I didn't want the attention for that. I didn't want the pity. I didn't want to be bald. But I put my head down and remembered why I was doing this: my kids (who were only five and two at the time.)

But this was my new reality. This was now part of my story.

Someone recommended I cut my hair to a short hairstyle to mentally adjust to this idea of less hair. I decided that would be a great place to start. I cried quite a bit after that cut, and it hadn't even started to fall out. I think it was the first of many out-of-control moments in my life. But I got up each day and told myself that this blip of time would feel sooo small very soon, so just keep moving forward. So I did. One day at a time. One foot in front of the other. Some days one moment at a time.

A month later my first chemo treatment began. The doctor said that my hair was likely to fall out, but probably not for fourteen to twenty-one days at least. I kept thinking I would be one to beat the odds and it would not happen to me. I thought about what it might feel like or what I would look like. I lost most of my hair on day fourteen. I woke up one day to my hair coming out in clumps as I ran my hands through it. I decided then it was time to get my first and hopefully only buzz cut.

I went to my hair gal, and she helped me create the most epic recreation of Britney Spears's head shave incident. I took pics in a hoodie with a bald head and an umbrella as well as the pic of me "shaving my own head." It immediately went on Facebook, and people were not sure what to think. On one hand, they were laughing because it was funny, but on the other, they were shocked because up to that point, the world didn't know my health situation. I wanted them to be laughing—not because I wasn't afraid, but more because life is truly what we focus on. I didn't cry that day, oddly enough, I think because I was laughing too much.

Not even a week later, I woke up feeling like I had needles in my head (like the guy in that old horror movie *Hellraiser*. I know—bad visuals, but that was what it felt like. I did cry that day, but in pain. I had my husband completely shave my head, and in two minutes it didn't physically hurt anymore. But the pain, mentally, was like a ton of bricks. I cried as the shower water washed over my bald head. I let myself feel what I needed to feel that day and any other day my lack of hair bothered me, but after I acknowledged my feelings, I got up and put on a cute wig or scarf and did life as a thirty-year-old mom.

Losing your hair is not something anyone really wants for their path of cancer, but if you find yourself in this space and welcomed into the club nobody wants to be a part of, embrace it and do the best you can for the moment you are in. They are not all good days, but they are not all bad either. Stay focused on what is real and what is important and what is in front of you today, and you will make it through.

INSIGHTS FROM
SHARED STORIES:

- Always trust your instincts.
- Dense breasts need more tests.
- Get up and go even when you don't feel like it.
- Find a doctor who is uplifting and respects you.
- Be the one who makes the others around you smile.
- Celebrate your milestones by doing something to help others.
- Be like Mario Andretti and walk around the nurses' station after your surgery.
- All breast cancer radiation machines should have eyes, eyelashes, and a smile.

CHAPTER SIX:

Nutrition—Eat Like You Love Yourself

Your body is your temple, keep it pure and
clean for the soul to reside in.
—B. K. S. Iyengar

I need to start by saying I'm *not* a nutritionist, and I'm not suggesting you eat a specific way, but I can tell you what you put into your body does matter. It doesn't have to be some crazy change, but just small changes over time. You may even want to consult with a nutritionist or a doctor. Have some tests run. We are all unique individuals, and our bodies all work differently! I'm hoping that sharing what I'm doing and some of the research I have done will help you get started on a healthier path. But of course, always consult with your doctor if you have any questions.

My nutrition has *completely* done a 180 since my diagnosis. I used to eat low carb (meaning basically no fruits, whole grains, or fiber) and higher protein. I used to eat animal protein pretty much with every meal. The second I was diagnosed, I went plant based. In fact, for a little bit, I was scared to put anything in my body. Think about it like this: animals instinctively know when they are sick, the way to heal themselves is *not* to eat. My intuition was telling me I needed to change the way I was eating.

"Let food be thy medicine
and medicine be thy food"—Hippocrates

Since then, I've been doing my research on the foods I put into my body, and I'm so happy I made that decision. I do allow myself wild-caught fish when I'm out (two to four times a month). I guess I would call myself a flexible vegan. Here are some specifics I have discovered in some of the research I have done with nutrition and breast cancer.

More Plants. I'm not saying you have to go vegan; remember, I'm a bit extra. But if you eat more plant-based foods, you may lower your chances of getting breast cancer and the recurrence of breast cancer. Please know I'm not suggesting fake meats with the ingredient list a mile long. I'm talking about healthy plant foods such as fruits, vegetables, whole grains, nuts, seeds, beans, lentils, and soy products (more on soy in a minute). Fruits and vegetables are also an important part of a diet that will help you control your weight, which is key for keeping breast cancer from coming back.

Embrace whole grains. Thank God! Anyone out there like me that used to swear off all this? I did. Now, I happily enjoy my avocado toast in the morning on delicious organic spelt bread without any guilt. Here's why. When you add unprocessed wheat, rye, oats, corn, bulgur, rice, and barley to your diet, it may lower the chances the cancer will return. These foods have nutrients called phytochemicals, which are believed to protect cells from damages that could lead to cancer. They can also help protect against cardiovascular disease. Some cancer survivors may have higher odds of cardiovascular disease in part because some treatments can damage the heart. I have left sided breast cancer, so this is definitely a concern for me. So you better believe I am embracing the whole grain.

Fats. We're not talking about healthy fats here like avocado, olive oil, and nuts. We're talking about the bad fat—saturated and trans fat. Studies from American Institute for Cancer say it may play a role in the growth of breast tumors, but the research is far from clear. Your best bet is to limit saturated fats and trans fats (which come in foods like beef, butter, cheese, ice cream, fried foods, and commercial baked goods).

When it comes to protein, go for lean kinds such as fish and chicken. Another added benefit is that this will help your waistline.

Fiber. This is an important one: How much fiber are you consuming daily? Most people get this naturally if they are eating plenty of whole grains, fruits, vegetables, and legumes. I'm pretty sure I wasn't getting the recommended amount of 20 to 25g of fiber per day. Plus, fiber is good for your overall health, especially your blood sugar levels, heart, and digestive tract. I read from a Harvard study that fiber intake has been associated with a lower risk of estrogen and progesterone receptor-positive breast cancer, which is what I was diagnosed with. I wish I had been eating more fiber back in the day!

Vitamin D. Another super-important one. (Who am I kidding? *All* of this is important.) Studies from the Cleveland Clinic show a link between low levels of this nutrient and higher chances of breast cancer. If you live in an area where you are not seeing the sun a lot, like me (I'm a Michigan girl), you definitely should be supplementing. Get your levels checked with your doctor. It may play a role in the growth of tumors. You can add it to your diet with foods like salmon, oysters, herring, mackerel, and sardines—although I would rather supplement than eat sardines!

Soy. OMG, soy! Let's put the soy controversy to rest. Soy-based foods such as tofu, soy milk, and edamame, have chemicals called phytoestrogens, which are similar to estrogen. This previously raised fears in women with breast cancer because soy uses estrogen as fuel to grow, but the latest studies from Dana-Farber Cancer Institute, show soy doesn't raise cancer risk. It may even lower the odds the disease will return. Here are three important things to know:

- Phytoestrogens are structurally different and significantly weaker than human estrogen.
- Phytoestrogens do not turn into estrogen when you eat them.

- Soy doesn't cause breast cancer, but in fact it may offer protection from breast cancer or recurrence of breast cancer.

Bonus is that phytoestrogens help some women manage hot flashes that come along with menopause. It's a great source of protein, fiber, calcium, iron and magnesium. Just make sure to purchase organic, non-GMO soy products.

Flavonoids. Dark chocolate, anyone? It's one of the top ten foods with high flavonoids. These chemicals, which you find in certain plants, are linked to lower breast cancer odds. The evidence is strongest for two specific types, flavonols and flavones, especially for women who are past menopause. You can find flavonoids in berries, red cabbage, kale, onions, broccoli, tea (I have a chapter dedicated to tea—it's *that* important), and more. Flavones come in parsley, celery, and drinks with chamomile. Keep in mind: don't overdo the dark chocolate. There are many things that will say "dark chocolate," but it's not really...and of course, purchase the organic kind. I also make sure it's 88 percent cacoa.

Carotenoids. This one makes me happy because I think I could live on sweet potatoes. This is another type of phytochemical in plant-based food linked to lower breast cancer risk. You can get it from orange, yellow, dark green vegetables, and fruits. Look to include more carrots, pumpkins, winter squash, spinach, kale, sweet potatoes, and cantaloupe in your diet.

Phenolic compounds. I add this every morning to my smoothie in the form of flax seeds. Studies from Cancer Therapy Advisory show these types of chemicals may lower your chances of breast cancer and in some cases slow tumor growth. I'll take that! Add more to your diet in the form of garlic, green tea (here we go again with the tea), soybeans, and flaxseed. Fruits and vegetables that have them include broccoli, cabbage, tomato, eggplant, cucumber, and watermelon.

Intermittent fasting. The last thing I want to briefly talk about is intermittent fasting. I think it's something you may want to consider.

It's way less complicated than you might think. It's just the hours you eat and the hours you don't. Allowing your digestion a break is so good for you. It doesn't need to be anything extreme. Most days of the week, my kitchen is closed at 6:00 p.m. I don't eat after that. Then I start eating the next morning around 8:00 a.m., so I fast for about fourteen hours a day.

Recent animal studies from Memorial Sloan Kettering Cancer Center, have shown a decrease in risk for cancer or a decrease in cancer growth rates. These studies indicate this may be due to the following effects from fasting:

- Decreased blood glucose production.
- Stem cells triggered to regenerate the immune system.
- Balanced nutritional intake.
- Increased production of tumor-killing cells.

So, something to consider.

I get asked all the time what I eat in a typical day, so I thought I would share:
- Breakfast is typically oatmeal and berries or avocado toast.
- After my workout around 10am I have a loaded smoothie: 1 scoop of plant-based protein (you can find my favorite in the resource page at jendelvaux.com/bookresources), flax & chia seeds, amla berry powder, almond milk, nut butter and a banana.
- Lunch around 1pm is always a huge salad (I change it up, but here's an example): Mixed greens, tofu, avocado, roasted sweet potatoes, roasted cabbage, cumin black beans, walnuts, roasted chickpeas with a little hummus or salsa for dressing, topped with nutritional yeast.
- Dinner changes up a bit, but I try to make something with onions, mushrooms & cruciferous vegetables, which are true super foods when it comes to healing cancer.

Sometimes it's a soup or chili, roasted vegetables with tofu, or maybe even another big salad. Kitchen closes by 6pm, so I can fast for at least 13 hours.

THE TEN BREAST SUPERFOODS FROM THE BOOK: *BREASTS, THE OWNER'S MANUAL*, DR. KRISTI FUNK

1. Cruciferous Vegetables and Leafy Greens
2. Dietary Fiber
3. Berries
4. Apples
5. Tomatoes
6. Mushrooms
7. Garlic, Onions, Leeks, Shallots, Chives, Scallions
8. Turmeric and Spices
9. Seaweed
10. Cacao

All the research/studies from this chapter can be found in the reference page at the end of the book.

CHAPTER SEVEN:

Tea Time—Cancer Hates It

Where there is tea, there is hope.
—Wing Pinero

It may seem odd to dedicate an entire chapter to tea, but it's so important in your treatment plan that I wanted to give it its own chapter. With all the research I've been doing, I keep seeing that this will one day be part of the breast cancer treatment plan. So, steep your tea, and let's dive in.

All I needed to see was this one study from the book, *Cancer Hates Tea*, to jump on the tea train. This study suggested the possibility of regular tea consumption, three to five cups per day, may be preventive against recurrence of cancer. Women who drank more than three cups per day experienced 57 percent fewer relapses of breast cancer than those who only drank one cup. Ummmmm…HELLO. I immediately ordered some tea. I'll share my favorites in a bit.

Cancer has its weaknesses. Antioxidants. Foods like vegetables, fruits, whole grains, legumes (peas, beans, and lentils), nuts, seeds, and spices are fantastic antioxidants. So why tea? Let me explain. Tea ranks higher than most fruits and vegetables in antioxidant potential and vitamin C and K content. Various medical studies from different countries around the world have reported on tea as an anti-inflammatory agent as well as a selective immune-system booster in pursuing anticancer mechanisms.

Green tea is made from the leaves of the Camellia sinensis, a plant native to parts of Asia. The same plant also produces white, oolong, and black teas. Each type represents a progressive stage in the leaves' development. Green comes after white and appears to be the stage when certain compounds are at their highest concentrations. When you steep your tea, you're extracting its powerful nutrients. Think of it as a healing blanket for your cells.

What's in tea that makes it so special?

- Polyphenols make up 40 percent of the active ingredient in your tea. Tea polyphenols are among the most efficient of all free radical scavengers, and they're more readily absorbed than most other antioxidants found in plant-based foods. Cancer aside, they may improve digestion, brain function, and blood sugar levels, as well as protect against blood clots and heart disease.
- Flavonoids have beneficial anti-inflammatory effects and protect your cells from oxidative damage that can lead to disease. Remember we discussed this in the nutrition chapter?
- Catechins are natural antioxidants that help prevent cell damage and provide other benefits. They can reduce the formation of free radicals in the body, protecting cells and molecules from damage.
- EGCg. The most dynamic of the catechins is epigallocatechin gallate (EGCg). Studies have shown that its antioxidant capacity is 100 times more powerful than vitamin C in protecting DNA from damage by free radicals. Also, it is twice as powerful as resveratrol.
- Theanine, also known as L-theanine, is an amino acid found primarily in green and black teas. It's said to help ease anxiety and stress and reduce insomnia. Anything that reduces insomnia—I'm in!

Quick note on caffeine: The effects of caffeine in tea are often reported as being different from the effects of caffeine in coffee. This is thought to be because of the theanine that's in it. When you have decaf green tea, it has fewer antioxidants. So, I stick with the caffeinated teas and have my last cup by 3:00 p.m.

If you want more info on tea, I highly recommend getting the book *Cancer Hates Tea*, by Maria Uspenski, founder of the Tea Spot (where I get my loose-leaf tea from). This book also serves as a reference on the benefits of tea in this chapter.

Remember, not all teas are created equal. Store-bought tea bags and ready-to-drink teas have a minimal amount of polyphenols. So stick with properly sourced loose-leaf teas. My other favorite place to get my teas is from Pique Teas, which sells tea crystals. They extract the bioactive compounds in teas and super plants at cold-to-low temperatures for up to eight hours. This artisanal process gently extracts natural antioxidants and phytonutrients and preserves them in a whole form, where all beneficial compounds are present. This is the purest way to extract phytonutrients in plants for maximum efficacy. You can access my pique tea link to receive a discount at jendelvaux.com/bookresources.

The reason loose-leaf or tea crystals are better is that tea bags can also accumulate toxic mold in harmful quantities. These toxins have been linked to a range of long-term health issues. How crazy is that?

Listen, if you don't get in all five cups of tea every day, don't stress about it. One cup is already better than none. Maybe just remind yourself of the benefit of getting in three to five cups equals less chance of recurrence. People always ask me if I still drink coffee. Yes, I have one cup in the morning and then switch over to tea.

CHAPTER EIGHT:

Exercise—Move Your Body, Sis!

And when you get the choice to sit it out or dance.
I hope you dance…I hope you dance…
—Lee Ann Womack

Imagine if there was a magic pill that would make you feel better mentally and physically. It would help offset any of the side effects from treatment. And may make it less likely that the cancer would return. And maybe even help you to live a longer and fuller life! Would you take it? I'm assuming that's a big "Hell yes" from all of you!

That magic pill, my friends, is called exercise. Okay, so maybe it takes more work than just swallowing a pill but trust me—exercise is life changing. Especially for someone dealing with a cancer diagnosis.

I believe that exercise is one of your most important cancer treatments. Not only for your health, but your mindset and attitude too. Exercise is literally therapy to me. Listen, it didn't used to be. I used to hate it. So if the thought of exercise sounds torturous to you, I get it. I've been there. But you can turn that around. Think about it this way: exercising is *nothing* compared to what you have already endured with your cancer treatments. Promise! Exercising can literally save your life.

I scheduled my radiation treatments early in the morning and promised myself thirty minutes in my gym. Sometimes it would be a ride on my bike, maybe a strength training session, yoga, or a walk. Sometimes I would just lie there and meditate for thirty minutes. This was pure therapy for me. It helped me to get the stress out. Sometimes after a sweat session, I would just cry on my mat, but it gave me the confidence I needed to do the hard things. It made me realize I could get through anything.

Not sold yet? Keep reading for the benefits, how much exercise you need, and how to work it into your day.

Benefits:

- It can help avoid or reduce some side effects of cancer treatment, such as fatigue, weight gain, osteoporosis, and lymphoedema.
- Exercise improves your long-term health, reducing the risk of heart attacks and strokes, and it may reduce the risk of the cancer coming back.
- It helps your mental well-being by reducing anxiety, stress, and depression and improving your mood.
- It may prevent or reduce the loss of muscle tone and general fitness that can happen during and after treatment.

Still not sold? What's stopping you? Are you worried that it might not be safe? There's evidence to the contrary. For instance, when researchers from Mayo Clinic reviewed sixty-one studies involving women with stage 2 breast cancer, they found that a combination of aerobic and resistance exercise was not only safe, but it also improved health outcomes.

Exercise helps you manage your weight, which is an important cancer risk factor. There's also increasing evidence that being overweight may lead to a higher risk of cancer recurrence, which I think is literally the biggest fear of any woman who has been diagnosed—the fear of it coming back. Bonus: it improves your mood!

Are you ready to get started?

How Much Exercise

The physical activity guidelines for people with cancer are similar to those recommended for everyone: 150 minutes of moderate-intensity activity (that's only twenty-one minutes a day) or seventy-five minutes of vigorous-intensity activity every week.

Quick side note: obviously you need to be cleared to do so by your surgeon. But the second you get the green light, go for it!

If you are just starting out, it's best to start slowly with an activity you enjoy and gradually build up the amount you do. I think sometimes the reason people hate to exercise is that they do something that their body isn't ready for. This can then cause so much soreness that they never want to go back.

For example, if you enjoy walking, start walking a short distance regularly. Then gradually begin to build up the distance, number of times a day you walk, and the speed at which you walk.

There are so many apps out there that can monitor your progress and keep you challenged and motivated. Setting realistic goals, keeping a record of how much activity you do, and sharing your progress with other people may help you stay motivated. I have an accountability group for women who have been diagnosed with cancer and are ready to get their health on track. You can request to join the Facebook group in the resource page at jendelvaux.com/bookresources or go to: https://www.facebook.com/groups/nottodaycancerfittofight.

Another tactic to get started is just making exercise part of your everyday activities:

- Energetic housework. Put on some good music or listen to a podcast. It makes it more fun.
- Park your car a little farther away from the shops or work and walk the rest of the way.
- Use the stairs instead of an elevator.
- Sit less and stand more. You could walk around when talking on the phone. I have a standing desk that I love.

One more stat for you before we move into exercise options:

Thirty minutes of exercise five times per week is all one needs to achieve a 40% reduction in breast cancer recurrence and death, according to the studies from breastcancer.org. Unbelievable, right?

Okay, now grab your calendar and schedule it in your week. Just like you would a doctor's appointment.

Exercise ideas:
- Walking
- Bike riding or cycling
- Strength training (remember, this should be done two or three times a week)
- Running
- Yoga
- Pilates
- Barre
- Tai Chi
- Dancing
- Cardio
- Core

We all love Netflix, right? What if there was something similar to Netflix, but with workouts that you could follow along with? Guess what? There is! If you need this and are interested in learning more, reach out here: coachjennyd@gmail.com. I can help you get started.

PART THREE:

Life after Your Diagnosis— Own Your Power

You beat cancer by how you live, why you live,
and in the manner of which you live.
—Stuart Scott

My "Not Today Cancer" team at the Bee Brave Event.

CHAPTER NINE:

How to Get Back to Your New "Normal"

Every day changes us. And some days change us a lot. You are a different person now, especially after a cancer diagnosis. And your life should reflect that. Cancer has given you a permission slip to undergo radical life change. Change is good! Embrace this new season of change. Embrace the new you that you are becoming.
—Chris Wark, Beat Cancer Daily

One of the hardest things for me to accept when I was first diagnosed was that I knew this would change me forever. I had always thought I was invincible, and when you are hit with a cancer diagnosis, you realize how short life can be. Also, I'm a super-social person. I love to throw cocktail parties (that usually turn into dance parties late into the night) and entertain. I also love a good bottle of wine. Listen, I promise I don't have a drinking problem, but Darren and I love to cook (well, I cook; he cleans up after me), listen to music, and share a bottle of red. And we always have a weekly date night that of course includes a glass or two of bubbly. Sadly, I knew that was going to have to stop—or at least slow down.

In fact, I fought it for a bit.

I started researching breast cancer and alcohol, and unfortunately, the stats are not great. And the medication I was on to shut down my ovaries said to avoid alcohol. I remember calling my doctor and saying (I'm actually embarrassed about it now), "I'm not sure if I want to do this if I can't enjoy date night with my husband…or girls' night out."

I know…it sounds ridiculous, but again, being social and enjoying a glass of wine or two was fun for me and made me happy.

I also talked with a lot of women to see how they handled it. Some stopped altogether, some had no idea about the research and have always enjoyed their adult beverage, and some cut back. I cut back and worked on my beliefs/worries. I truly believe that if you are enjoying a glass of wine with friends or on a date night without having any guilt or worries, you are totally fine. I think if you have a drink and then you are up at night with fear over it, then you shouldn't do it. Our minds are powerful.

Let's take my husband as an example. He was diagnosed with brain cancer in 2009. It started out as a grade 2, came back eighteen months later as a grade 3 (another surgery, chemo, radiation, a ton of complications, and almost died that year), went eight years, and came back again in 2019 as a grade 4. And here he is today, still doing awesome. You know how I'm extra and made all the changes, right? He honestly didn't change a thing. He still loves his Manhattans and has the biggest sweet tooth of anyone I've ever known. Although one thing I guess he did change is his attitude. Happiest person on earth. He wakes up singing. Laughs every day and has so much confidence—and truly lives without any fear of the future. It's incredible to see.

So today, yes, I am a new person, and honestly, better. I'm still me. But a happier version. I enjoy each and every day (I mean 98 percent of them—nobody is perfect), I slowed way down, I don't stress about the little things, it brought Darren and me even closer, and I am way more spiritual. I pray every day. I remember my girlfriend Chalene Johnson saying, "It's kind of crazy to think how highly God must think of you to know that you can handle all of this. I guess He wasn't sure if you got the message about cancer being your calling/purpose—so he decided to send the message a little louder." I hear you loud and clear now, God! I can honestly say, this new path I'm on, helping women navigate a diagnosis, is truly my calling. Finding purpose behind a cancer diagnosis I believe helps so much in getting you through it. I've heard incredible stories of women who have started a 5K, or become a cancer coach, or created head wraps, and so much more. Finding purpose behind the madness makes it all seem okay.

When October came around, breast cancer awareness month, I knew I wanted to do something to support it. I started searching for a run/walk in my area. I heard from a local breast cancer thriver of the Bee Brave 5K event. It was exactly what I was looking for. If you are local, you can get the details at jendelvaux.com/bookresources.

It was short notice, but I was able to get a team of about ten people together. We all wore shirts that said, "Not Today Cancer," and of course it gave some of us a chance to wear fun pink tutus.

I had no idea what to expect other than it was out in the country. There were kids with signs leading us through a farm and up to where the race was being held. They were cheering us along and holding up their signs of support. It was amazing! I didn't realize this event would bring on so many emotions for me. I had to fight back some of the tears. I certainly didn't want my lashes to fall off before the event.

Before the walk began, the organizers invited different people to share their stories of hope. It was very inspiring listening to these women. It was awesome to see how large the teams were of these brave warriors.

After the walk, many of the people had tailgate parties to congratulate the walkers and their teams. Next year we will definitely be upping our game! In fact, I'm officially helping to organize the event as well. Volunteering and giving back is another way to help in the healing process.

To find walks or runs in your area to support advancement in breast cancer treatment, search "breast cancer walks or runs near me" on Google.

After treatment is complete, sometimes new emotions can set in— worry and fear of it coming back. You don't have weekly or monthly appointments with doctors and nurses caring for you. Life goes on as usual for family and friends. And you are kind of like...woah, what just happened? I think we are on autopilot through the tough stuff, and then, when all that stops, you are like, okay, now what? Does everything just go back to normal?

In my opinion and experience, I do think this is when the true healing begins. I gave myself grace during the treatments for the most part, but when that was over, I took control! Here are some things to help you get back to your new and improved normal.

1. Take charge; control your fear: One of the most common things I hear is the worry/fear of it coming back. Every ache or pain, you may be concerned that it's cancer. This is very understandable. I get it, but here are my thoughts on it. You know I've discussed throughout this book that our minds are super powerful. If you are constantly worried about some new ache or pain, talk to your doctor. Don't hold it in and have constant fear over it. It's probably nothing, and when you talk to your doctor, she/he will either relieve your fear or maybe run a test, which may turn out to be nothing. Your energy is important, and it's my belief that if you are in a constant state of worry and stress, that can cause disease. If you are taking control of your diagnosis, meaning making changes with your nutrition, exercise, adding in mediation, and working on your mindset, this will help alleviate the fear of it coming back. And for the love, have some fun! We have one freaking life to live. Do not live in a state of constant worry. I think people who don't make any changes after the diagnosis struggle with fear and worry the most—unless they truly believe that the treatment they received was enough, like Darren.

2. Consider therapy. When treatment is finished, some people can feel depressed, whether it be from a new medication or not being constantly monitored anymore by

doctors and nurses. They can feel alone with their feelings. I highly recommend going to therapy and talking through everything you just went through. Get those emotions out. Remember, we want emotions to move through us. It's important to feel them all and then release them. I do believe that stress, worry, and anxiety can play a role in causing cancer, so this is a good time to get to the bottom of why this happened in the first place.

You can also try working with an energy healer. This was hugely powerful for me. I didn't even understand what it all was, but I just know that it completely relaxed me and helped me to feel calm. It feels like a massage for your energy.

Energy healing is a holistic practice where healers channel universal life force (or healing energy) into a patient to help balance, heal, and remove blockages from the body. Flow, balance, harmony, and vitality within the body can be restored and maintained during a treatment. Energy medicine includes a variety of holistic healing modalities like Reiki energy healing, light therapy, acupuncture, reflexology, Thai massage, tapping, and more.

3. Your new body. I had a lumpectomy and radiation. So yes, my breast that had cancer is slightly different, but not too noticeable, so I wanted to share the story from Shannon Burrows (IG @shannonmburrows) and how she handled it.

I was diagnosed with high-grade DCIS (ductal carcinoma in situ) on July 13, 2017, at the age of forty-five. After further discussions with my general surgeon and the results of an Oncotype test (56), I made the decision to take the route of having a double mastectomy as my treatment plan, since I was not interested in visiting this season again. I was very confident in that decision and never thought what my breasts would look like or how my husband would see them because all I wanted was the cancer out of my body and the likelihood of recurrence to be lessened. To be completely transparent, once I made that decision, I went into denial and focused on scheduling every appointment needed prior to surgery, work, and telling our daughter. After waking up from my double mastectomy and seeing my chest for the first time, I was surprisingly shocked at the appearance. I had visions of my chest being completely concave, but it wasn't. When I finally made it home and was able to get into my "new real life," scars and all, I remember looking at my incisions and thinking, "You are a rockstar! You just kicked cancer's a$$! You have not only gone through in vitro fertilization and created a human inside of you, you've beat cancer!" Yes, I look at those scars, and it's a reminder of how far I've come. It's a reminder to me that when I have those days of feeling like the world is crashing in on me, I am bigger than those struggles. I fought a fight I wasn't even prepared for. As for my husband, whenever I would ask him how he felt, because I was mortified to be naked in front of him, his response was he didn't even see the scars. He tells me my scars don't define me. He's right—they don't define you, but they sure are a constant reminder of how brave and strong we truly are. I look at my scars daily as a reminder that they are helping me serve my purpose, to help and support other women navigate their breast cancer season because someone else believed in how strong I was too. As my favorite childhood icon said, "You are braver than you believe, stronger than you seem, and stronger than you think!"

4. Hopefully, you are making personal changes to help bring joy into your life. Here's my recipe for joy:
    - Listen to music.
    - Write down what you are grateful for daily.
    - Listen to a guided meditation.
    - Make it a point to laugh every day.
    - Give back.
    - Quit being so serious. Let Loose. Have fun.

- Turn off the news.
- Slow down and be kind to others.
- Get out of your sweats and put on one of your favorite outfits.
- Treat yourself—massage, pedi and mani, a new outfit.

A happy heart will do you good. It's like medicine for the soul.

5. Knowledge is power! Getting to know your girls is so important. Especially after dealing with a breast cancer diagnosis. Keep in mind, they may feel lumpy, tender or thick for a bit after surgery and treatment. Just keep an eye on it and let your doctor know if there's any changes that you are worried about. I did an ultrasound about 6 months after because I was concerned, but it was only scar tissue, thank God.

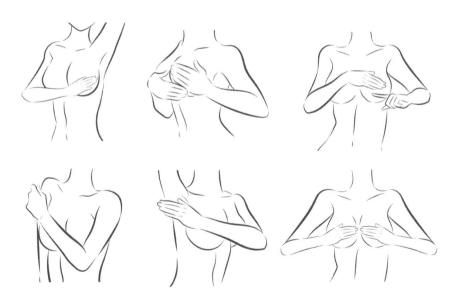

Okay, let's get to it, "Feel it on the first" self-breast exam. Unless you are still having your period, then do it one week after (that's when you are least lumpy and tender). This should only take a few minutes.

First you want to VISUALLY examine your breasts:

1. Look for puckering, dimpling or change in size, shape or symmetry.
2. Check to see if your nipples are turned in (inverted).
3. In the first posture, put your hands on your hips and push in so you are flexing your chest. Any dents or bumps?
4. Second posture raise both hands over your head - Give them a good stare and get to know your breasts. Does everything look normal?

Alright time to get handsy…You can either be doing this lying down or standing in the shower, whatever is more comfortable for you. You may want to use lotion or shower gel to make this easier:

1. Up and down the length of your breasts vertically
2. Left to right across the breast
3. Concentrically in circles like a target sign
4. Radially like spokes on a wheel

Start with your left breast and raise the left hand behind your head to help flatten the tissue. First using the pads, not the fingertips, of your three middle fingers for the exam. Start at your armpit and then move along to your breast using whatever pattern from above. Repeat 3xs and use different pressure levels. Light, medium, and a little bit harder. Gently squeeze your nipple…If you squeeze out bloody or clear-like fluid, or if discharge is spontaneous, see your doctor.

REPEAT on the right breast.

Don't freak out over every lump or bump, sometimes it can be normal, especially during your period.

Here are some signs that you'll want to contact your doctor and get further testing:

- A hard lump or knot near your underarm.
- Changes in the way your breasts look or feel, including thickening or prominent fullness that is different from the surrounding tissue.
- Dimples, puckers, bulges or ridges on the skin of your breast.
- Redness, warmth, swelling or pain.
- Itches, scales, sores or rashes.
- A recent change to a nipple being pushed in (inverted) instead of sticking out.
- Bloody nipple discharge.

Keep in mind, this may be due to something other than cancer. Don't panic, but make sure you get it checked out.

CHAPTER TEN:

Love and Marriage—in Sickness and in Health...

*Cancer cannot cripple love, it cannot shatter
hope, it cannot conquer the spirit.*
—Unknown

Let's be real: cancer isn't sexy. It changes you, and it can change your relationship. After surgeries and treatments, a number of issues arise, both physically and emotionally. These include feeling uncomfortable in your new body and being betrayed by your body. Our breasts tried to kill us, so it doesn't feel sexy anymore. Less interest in sex, dry or atrophied vagina (thanks to menopause and AIs), which makes sex painful. Or maybe your roles have changed from husband and wife to patient and caretaker. That happened to us when Darren was going through his treatments. But there is hope. Here's what has helped us:

#1. Talk to your doctor, or better yet, find a doctor who specializes in menopause/sex health after cancer.

A lot of cancer centers offer this. In my area I found a concierge practice, True Women's Health, that specializes in this. I've learned so much. There are many things we can still do. I thought since I was diagnosed with an ER/PR positive breast cancer, I was out of luck. But there's some hope.

Here are some of the recommendations from my doctor because I'm dealing with full-blown menopause (dryness, tightness, hot flashes, no sex drive, etc.):

- One option is to purchase a dilator that gradually stretches a tight vagina (my doctor recommended the Milli from milliforher.com).
- Use lubricants. I use Honor Everyday Balm. It hydrates, conditions, and replenishes intimate skin. It provides all-natural relief for dryness that comes along with the lovely menopause symptoms.
- There are also vaginal lasers such as the MonaLisa Touch, which stimulate collagen formation and improve moisture in just a few sessions. I haven't done this yet, but I'm considering it.
- For hot flashes I am doing acupuncture, which has so many benefits (more on this later) and started taking Menopause Miracle (non-estrogen symptom relief). You can access this at jendelvaux.com/bookresources.

#2 Have open communication

I was very open and honest with Darren. I explained to him exactly how I was feeling. I think sometimes we're embarrassed or feel shame over how we are feeling in our own bodies. But I promise, this will help and may even bring you closer together. They will now understand what's going on. If you don't share, they may take it personally and the wrong way. Or maybe even consider couples therapy. We love therapy.

Therapy is not a negative experience. It's the most rewarding thing you can do for your marriage.

In fact, we create dates out of our therapy sessions. We may not be loving each other as we are walking in, but typically we're holding hands on the way out.

#3: Date your significant other (our specialty!)

This is one of my favorite tips.

Whether you go out for dinner, stay in for dinner, take a walk, or go to a movie, treat it like a date. Get ready, make yourself look good, put on some music, pick out your outfits together—have fun with it! No matter what's going on at home, at work, or in any other part of your life, you need to just commit to putting it all aside for a few hours to focus on each other.

Do not—I repeat, do not—interrupt your date to discuss negative topics in your relationship. This is supposed to be a release from the day-to-day grind.

In our situation, we don't want to waste time dealing with petty problems, but they exist. But with a cancer diagnosis, at times our dates can be pretty emotional. We embrace that. It brings us closer. We have had some of our deepest conversations over wine and dinner. One unforgettable night in 2019 after Darren's third brain surgery, where his brain cancer had progressed to a grade 4, we got really deep. I was making dinner, we had music on, and he poured us a glass of wine. We were listening to acoustic covers, a song came on, and he said, "I want this song at my funeral." I attempted to brush it off like I typically did when he would try to discuss this, but he wouldn't let me this time. We talked about everything. His funeral. His death. If he had fear about dying. What would happen after? What he wanted to wear in his casket. Ummmm…of course, Mr. Worldwide wants it to be his tux. He also wants his funeral to be a black-tie event, invite only. LOL. I mean, come on. He even planned out who he would like me to marry. That's Darren for you—always wanting to make sure I'll be okay. There were tears and laughter and more tears and more laughter. It was so gut wrenching and beautiful at the same time. It's super important to have these conversations with your significant other. They are not easy, but you will not regret it, promise.

CHAPTER ELEVEN

Stories of Hope!

> *Women are like butterflies. We may look pretty and*
> *delicate, but baby we can fly through a hurricane.*
> —Betty White

Clarita Escalante. IG @the_clarita_escalante.
I was diagnosed with breast cancer. It was very devastating news, and it took a toll on my mental and physical health. Six months prior to my diagnosis, I donated eighteen inches to the Cancer Association. They make wigs and eyelashes for cancer patients, and six months forward, I was a patient as well. For the first year after my diagnosis and surgery, I lived in a "victim mode," asking myself the wrong question repeatedly: "Why me?"

One day I woke up and decided I couldn't live one more day, one more minute or second in this state, and I decided to do something about it. I went for a long run, I cried, and I asked God/Universe to guide me through the path I needed to follow.

At that moment, all the right podcasts, books, people, and things I needed in my journey started showing up. I went to school and decided to learn more about how the body functions and nutrition. At the beginning of my journey to health, I thought nutrition was going to solve it all and I would never hear the word *cancer* again. To my surprise, nutrition is important, but if you are not at peace with yourself you are not healthy either. You can be eating all the healthy foods, doing all the exercises, taking all the supplements, but if you are at war with yourself, you are never going to reach your optimal health. Holistic healing has been so crucial in my journey to health (including mind + body + soul). Even with all this work I have done for the past two years, every time I go for a checkup, all my fears come flooding back. But I find compassion for myself. I let out all my feelings and then I remember all the tools I have collected through my journey and start implementing them right away. What I thought at one point was the worst thing that had happened to me, I now see as a gift. It gave me the courage to deal with so many things I had bottled up inside me, and now I get to impact not only my life but also the people around me.

We all have ups and downs in life, and I want you to remember that our character, faith, purpose, and fulfillment in life get stronger at our most challenging times. If you are going through something challenging, just remember it is temporary and that there is always a message, a lesson, and a purpose that is specially for us.

My recovery ended in December 2018, but this has not stopped me from being a mom, friend, sister, coworker, runner, cyclist (indoor, LOL), and everything else I want to be. My life has been filled with gratitude, love, and inspiration. I am so grateful to have a second chance at life and to be able to share my story. I hope my story brings you comfort. If you are going through the same thing as me, I hope it brings peace, I hope you don't feel alone, I hope you feel empowered, and I hope you feel grateful for everything you have. Three years cancer free!

Lauren Tarpley. IG @typeaguidetocancer.
I was diagnosed with stage 2 Her2+ HR- breast cancer in September 2020 at the age of thirty-four.

I made sure to document my journey, and I turned that into a book to help others through their journeys, *Type A Guide to Cancer*. I needed to turn my pain into purpose, and I really enjoy engaging with and meeting new people.

I also find humor imperative in getting through this with positivity. Cancer is a racket and at times it can seem impossible, but just the simple act of laughing at yourself is medicinal.

Side note: I have her book and highly recommend it. I have the link to order at jendelvaux.com/bookresources.

Jen Rozenbaum. IG jenrozenbaum@gmail.com.
My name is Jen, and I was diagnosed in 2017 with stage 2B invasive lobular carcinoma. I had bilateral mastectomies with eight rounds of chemotherapy, ten years of Tamoxifen, and most recently a prophylactic oophorectomy.

From the minute I was diagnosed, I decided that this was happening for me, not to me. As a photographer with a small following of women, I knew I had to go public with my journey. I started doing Facebook lives and making YouTube videos every step of the way. Most importantly, I turned the camera on myself, taking selfies showing my body through all stages of surgery and healing. I wanted to show the realities of cancer, normalize breast cancer bodies, and give women hope that they can still smile and find joy even when struggling with their health.

After finishing treatment and then first feeling the tidal wave of emotions that came with my diagnosis, I realized cancer doesn't end when treatment does. Two years after my treatment ended, I wrote a book titled *What the Fuck Just Happened? A Survivor's Guide to Life after Breast Cancer*. In the book I address what it is like to put your life back together and find your new normal after cancer inevitably changes who you are.

By being part of and giving back to such a beautiful community of women, I have experienced an unbelievable exchange of hope and healing energy. Although I never wish cancer upon anyone, I can say that through my work, the women I have met have been the greatest gift I have ever been given. You can get the link for her book at jendelvaux.com/bookresources

Robyn Williams. IG @fitrobyn.
When I was told I would be doing chemo, my biggest concern was how it would affect my normal routine. I taught fitness classes five times a week and worked out at home; I didn't want to have to give any of that up. So I didn't.

I continued my fitness regime throughout all my chemo treatments; hair loss and all. And you know what? It was the absolute best thing I could've ever done. My fitness was one of the bright spots of my day, and I looked forward to it. It was my "normal" and felt like home amid a yucky time. Those endorphins are real and come in very handy. Now, don't misunderstand—I still rested when I needed to. But I never gave up moving! Not only did it help me sweat out all the toxins from the chemo, but I think the positive mindset I got from sticking to my routine was what helped the most.

Vicki Brooks. In 2013 I went in for my yearly mammogram. No big deal! This was routine. I was fifty-three years old, and I had been going in for yearly mammograms since I was forty. A few days after the mammogram, I received a call from the imaging center that they needed to do another mammogram. This had happened to me several times in the past. Once again, no big deal because I knew it would be nothing. I went in for the mammogram, and the technician said I needed to wait for the radiologist to read the results. If more tests needed to be run, they would do an ultrasound. She came back and said that they needed to do an ultrasound. This had never happened before, but I was still in the mindset that it was no big deal. After the ultrasound, the radiologist looked at me and said, "You need to get this checked out ASAP. You need to get a biopsy!" Well, now it *was* a big deal. I scheduled the biopsy that day for the following week. I went in for the biopsy, and several days later I got a call from my doctor that the biopsy was positive, and I had breast cancer. Not what I was expecting at all. I pretty much felt numb and totally overwhelmed. After lots of discussions with my family and friends, I made an appointment with the top breast surgeon in Dallas. I found out the cancer was small, non-invasive, and slow growing, which was a relief. I had a lumpectomy, radiation, and was prescribed the estrogen blocker Tamoxifen.

The first thing my oncologist said when I walked into her office was, "You need to start exercising." What? I just found out I have breast cancer and I have to go through surgery and treatments, and you want me to exercise? You see, I lived a very sedentary lifestyle and was about forty pounds overweight. I hated to sweat, hated sports, hated working out. I had never been very active in my life, and I sure didn't want to start now that I had a life-threatening disease! I didn't really follow her advice for several years. I actually gained some weight from eating for comfort. After that first year, I found out my daughter had decided to start trying to get pregnant. I was so excited about the prospect of becoming a grandmother for the first time. This was when I really started thinking about my health. I knew that at my weight, I would never be able to keep up with an active toddler, and I wanted to be the grandmother who played on the floor with the kids and ran around with them. I also started thinking about what my oncologist had said about exercise and cancer. How exercise greatly reduces the percentage of cancer returning. I had to do this for myself and for my family.

I joined Beachbody and started the journey to health and fitness. I lost forty pounds in a year, and by the time my first grandson was born, I was in the best shape of my life at age fifty-six. I continue to exercise daily, and I've maintained my weight loss within five to ten pounds this whole time. I stopped taking the Tamoxifen three years ago, and I am totally cancer free! Getting the diagnosis of breast cancer was a shock but was also a big wake-up call to take control of my health through healthy eating and exercise. I now have two very active grandsons, ages three and five, whom I keep quite often. If it weren't for the diagnosis of cancer and my oncologist's insistence that I exercise, I'm not sure if I would be able to keep up with those active little boys. I feel better at age sixty-two than I did in my forties!

Jessica Fishman. IG @_soulfulsunflower_.

My name is Jessica Fishman. I was diagnosed with breast cancer, triple negative, stage one, on September 30, 2020. My mom had passed away from ovarian cancer stage four in 2013 from the BRCA1 gene. For the last fifteen years of my life, I had been screened, yet it still missed my cancer. At thirty-four I was ready to prophylactically remove my breast, and when I did the first surgery, there were two tumors found. I have since over the last year had seven surgeries and twelve chemotherapy rounds. I have officially been cancer free for an entire year. I enjoy sharing my story because I advocated for myself, which saved my life. I found out I had the BRCA1 gene when I was twenty-one years old. Both my sister and I tested positive as well as my family. So we have always been on top of our screening, but sometimes you must be the squeaky wheel. You are never too young to be diagnosed with cancer, so don't think it can't happen to you. When you think something is wrong or you feel something, do not let it go. If your intuition is telling you something is wrong, get it checked. We know our body better than anybody else. Through my cancer journey, I started a nonprofit called soulfulsunflower, which gives away weekly boxes of safe skin care, beauty care, and hair care with a bunch of other little goodies that help during your cancer journey. It is my hope that we will all continue to pay it forward as I continue to grow this nonprofit. So many people are not only willing to donate, but so many people have received these amazing boxes that gave them a little bit of sunshine and a whole lot of hope.

If you want to learn more about her nonprofit or donate, you can email her at soulfulsunflowerinc@gmail.com.

M. K. Meredith. IG @mkmkmeredith. Author of the book *Not Your Usual Boob*.

My name is Mary Karen Meredith, and I'm a two-time breast cancer survivor. I was first diagnosed in 2015. Having lost my mom to breast cancer at a young age, I knew what to look for and luckily found the cancer early. Invasive ductal carcinoma on my left side. Between stage one and two with no lymph node involvement. After a double mastectomy and Tamoxifen, I was given the all clear.

Then, in 2017, I found another small lump under my skin. A recurrence. I had surgery to remove the cancer in the skin, removal of my ovaries, and radiation. This also included a medication switch to Aromasin. Along with these strategies, over the course of both diagnoses, I had eight reconstruction surgeries, including a DIEP Flap on the left side to correct encapsulation. This May will be five years cancer free. I can't wait! A milestone I'm really looking forward to.

I'm strong and healthy and feel more and more like myself every day.

What helped me get through everything was taking it all one moment at a time. And no matter what happened, always stepping forward. These two strategies were key for me. And these are strategies that continue to help me navigate this terrible and wonderful world. You can get the link for her book at jendelvaux.com/bookresources.

Kristie Arthur. IG @mama_arth23.
I was diagnosed with invasive lobular carcinoma, grade 2 ER+ HER2- on 12.31.20. I was just recovering from COVID, and it was a real shock. I am/was the healthy one. I have always been the caretaker, so this was a new journey for everyone in my family. My husband has had several health issues over the years and then was diagnosed with prostate cancer in 2019. He was just nine months out of finishing radiation when I was diagnosed.

I had a lumpectomy and then radiation. I missed chemo by two points. I am fifty years old and was very proud I had finished my journey with menopause by staying healthy and managing the symptoms. I never thought it would be me. Never.

It has been a long year. During radiation I went to work every day and powered through with the mindset that everything would be OK, and radiation was helping me heal.

Having a positive outlook got me through, but I would say "my tribe" was what really helped me. I have a huge family and group of friends that showed up. I let them help, I listened to their positive talk, and it really kept my spirits up. There is so much I could share, but one point I want to make is, shelter your mental health. The hormone suppressants really triggered my anxiety. I tried three different types before I decided I should pair it with Lexapro. Often people see taking antidepressants as a weakness. It has minimized the effects, along with several supplements, CBD oil, and regular exercise. I am so much better! It's not an easy journey, but it is your journey. Count on people, count on yourself, take bits and pieces of advice that work for you and make it your own.

Elizabeth Cox. IG @elizabeth.cox915.
A cancer diagnosis is something I never thought could happen to me. As many other survivors will share, it turns your life upside down. It does not matter the stage you are diagnosed, single or married, family history or not, children or recently married. Cancer does not discriminate.

My mantra was "No Way but Through." I was getting to the other side and would be stronger because of it, but I had to go through the hard stuff. I remember talking to a new friend and asking at what point I become a "survivor," and she said, "The day you were diagnosed." I assumed there was a line you had to cross: finish chemo, surgery, or a year after diagnosis, but no. You are a survivor immediately. You are surviving each day. Her answer surprised me and inspired me. It comforted me.

On July 1, 2013, I was diagnosed with HER2 negative/ ER positive breast cancer in my right breast. I was thirty-one years old, married, and had a two-year-old daughter. No family history, and never had a mammogram. I found the lump on my own—or, rather, my daughter helped me find it by calling for me in the middle of the night for a hug. It was then that I felt pain from the lump. The next day I called my doctor, and the following days were followed with a mammogram, ultrasound, MRI, and lots of anxiety.

I received the official news that it was cancer while sitting in my office at work at 11:00 a.m., and by 2:00 p.m., I was sitting in the surgical oncologist's office. Due to the size of my tumor and location (by the nipple), a mastectomy was my only option. I elected to do a bilateral mastectomy even though my left side did not have cancer.

My bilateral (or double) mastectomy was scheduled for August 26, 2013. I met with many doctors—I had no idea there was a whole team that would be caring for me—surgical oncologist, plastic surgeon, oncologist, radiation oncologist. It was overwhelming, to say the least. However, I added one more to the mix and sought the expertise of a nutritionist. I knew there were multiple things I could not control, but if there was anything I could do to help in my survival and give my body a fighting chance of making it through surgery, chemo, radiation, and reconstructive surgery, I was going to do it.

The nutritionist advised me to eliminate all sugar and gave me a list of foods to add to my diet and those to eliminate. He took a hair sample, which was sent away, and days later reviewed with me the results on what my body was lacking and what supplements I should start. Again, it was overwhelming, but at least I was controlling something in my diagnosis. He explained how cancer cells "attach" to sugar and multiply. He provided me with in-depth information on how my body responded to certain foods, and it was helpful to understand better.

There were days that were difficult, but overall, it was a gift. I lived in the moment, I appreciated everything, big and small. I grew into a person who advocated for myself and understood the impact of food and exercise on my body. I became a different person, and I was okay. I was able to get through because of the support of my family, a positive attitude, and taking control of my lifestyle through nutrition, exercise, and meditation.

CHAPTER TWELVE:

Going the Extra Mile

Shoot for the Moon…Even if you miss you land among the Stars!
—*Norman Vincent Peale*

I was going to stop with chapter 11, because remember, I'm a numbers girl. But I'm also extra and over the top. So, I wanted to share with you all the things I have tried out to help in my healing. You don't need to do it all, but here are a few more things I have done to help in my journey that may help you as well.

Acupuncture. I started doing this weekly when I was first diagnosed. When my treatment was finished, I went biweekly and just recently switched to monthly. It has definitely helped me through the treatments. Acupuncture has been shown to ease the nausea, vomiting, dry mouth, fatigue, anxiety, depression, and immune suppression that can often accompany cancer treatment, according to studies from Pubmed. I also think it's helping me with the lovely menopause symptoms and with my bone health. Hormone-blocking meds are great for blocking estrogen, but not great on your bones and joints. If you are local, I highly recommend Stephen Durrel at Acupuncture of West Michigan. Check it out here or you can find it in the book resource page. https://www.acupunctureofwestmichigan.com.

Walking 10k steps a day! We sit *way* too much! Research from Dana-Farber Cancer institute, supports the idea that walking ten thousand steps a day contributes to reducing the risk of cancer and chronic diseases. Walk on lunch breaks, while talking on the phone, after dinner. Park farther away, take stairs instead of the elevator. So many ways to get extra steps in. Sometimes I even hop on my treadmill while I'm working.

Water Source. I did my research on water. All the things I learned are pretty crazy. So even though I have a water filter in my refrigerator (that doesn't do enough) and a reverse osmosis (that does too much), I purchased a Berkey water filter system. I love it *so* much. You can get more information for the Berkey system on the resource page at jendelvaux.com/bookresources.

We also recorded a podcast episode on water (Not Today Cancer, episode 127).

Infrared Sauna. I didn't start doing this until after my radiation treatments were complete. The benefits are incredible. By exposing your body to that heat, you're selectively killing or eradicating those less viable cells, those cancer cells, without hurting your normal cells. Infrared sauna may be useful because it can help you sweat, excrete toxins, and, in theory, eliminate cancer cells, which can't survive the heat. Plus, it's *so* relaxing! I listen to one of my favorite podcasts or read a book (my favorite books are under "Research") and relax.

Connection. I started connecting on Instagram with other women who were going through a breast cancer diagnosis or who had gone through it previously. I only connected with women who were super positive. You feel *so* alone when you are going through this. When you realize there are many, many, many more going through it previously and have survived, it helps immensely. If you have been diagnosed with cancer, you are more than welcome to join my cancer group, Not Today Cancer, stronger together: https://www.facebook.com/groups/nottodaycancer. It's not your typical sad cancer group. I try to keep it uplifting and educational.

Tapping. I started diving deep into my mental space. What I noticed had become a pattern was that I truly never dealt with my emotions. I stuffed them down. I always had to be the strong one. Unfortunately, emotions always find their way out one way or another. I worked with Kim Salter (IG @designthoughtstudio) where we did virtual tapping. She is amazing! It's like talk therapy, but you get to the bottom of things so much faster. She's very intuitive. I highly recommend her.

Be present. I started to slow way down and truly enjoy and appreciate life. I feel like we all go through the motions of life without looking at the beauty around us. I literally stopped to smell the flowers. I worked on really, truly being present. Especially the important moments. Put your phones away for a bit and just look around. It's pretty incredible.

Research. I read as much as I could about alternative ways to treat (besides the treatment that I was doing). Here are some books that I recommend:

- *Radical Remission*, Kelly A. Turner
- *Dying to Be Me*, Anita Moorjani
- *You Are the Placebo*, Dr. Joe Dispenza
- *Chris Beat Cancer*, Chris Wark
- *Breasts The Owner's Manual*, Dr. Kristi Funk

Remember, some of these books recommend more of the alternative approaches, but my preference is combining both.

Herbal meds. Thankfully, my acupuncturist is also an herbalist. A lot of his studies have been on cancer. Herbs have been used as medicine for thousands of years in China. *Herbs* can refer to a lot of different things in medicine, roots, flowers, leaves, stems, bark, seeds, and even stones. These are all therapeutic parts of plants that have natural healing properties that can promote well-being in both the body and the mind. Herbal medicine is an incredibly elegant system—hundreds of individual herbs can each have unique properties and functions. Individual herbs can definitely be used on their own, but they're more often combined into formulas to enhance their unique healing qualities and target particular conditions.

Hydro colon therapy. Also known as colon cleansing or colonic. The idea of this one freaked me out! I had to really think about it and do my research to see if it was worth it. I promise it is. I still do it every couple of months. You can listen to my experience and all the benefits in our podcast show, Not Today Cancer, episode 132. It will also be in the resource page of course.

Out with the old, In with the new. I'm talking about skincare of course. It's the largest organ in our body. It's time to take care of it. I went through my skincare and got rid of it all. Now I'm completely obsessed with KPS Essentials. They use powerhouse organic ingredients that you could literally eat, not that you'll want too, but it's that safe! You can get 10% off by using Jen10 at checkout. I'll share the link in the book resource page at jendelvaux.com/bookresources.

Ways that may help heal from radiation after you are completely finished (and, of course, check with your doctor):

- Chlorella. This detoxifies the body from radiation and chemotherapy. While they are, thankfully, effective at fighting certain types of cancers, they do take a toll on the body. Chlorella's high levels of chlorophyll have been shown to protect the body against UV radiation treatments while removing radioactive particles from the body. Its chlorophyll content is also an overall powerful cleansing agent for the body, as it aids in the processing of oxygen, cleanses the blood, primes the key elimination system of the body, and promotes growth and repair of tissues. My favorite brand is Organifi green juice because it's loaded with amazing, powerful ingredients like spirulina, wheatgrass, coconut water, ashwagandha, and more. You can get a discount with my link in the resource page at jendelvaux.com/bookresources.

- Supplementing with melatonin at night. Melatonin has beneficial properties for the reduction of radiation toxicity in healthy tissue and in the management of tumor responses to radiotherapy. The potent antioxidative effects of melatonin reduce oxidative DNA damage and cell death during radiation treatment.

- Infrared sauna. By exposing your body to that heat, you're selectively killing or eradicating those less viable cells, those cancer cells, without hurting your normal cells. The infrared sauna is useful because it can help you sweat, excrete toxins, and in theory eliminate cancer cells, which can't survive the heat. If you are local, I love Swet Sauna (https://www.swetsauna.com).

- Clay bath. Bentonite clay is a natural detoxing agent that can be used internally, externally with poultices, in full-body applications, and by taking detox clay baths. These are highly beneficial methods for detoxification, especially for cases of heavy metal poisoning and radiation buildup.

- Hyperbaric oxygen therapy. I have not done this. Sadly, we don't have it in my area unless it is done at the hospital. But if we did, I would be there in a heartbeat. HBOT makes it possible to minimize and even reverse your radiation symptoms. It uses powerful 100 percent oxygen at pressures above regular atmospheric pressure to stream oxygen through your bloodstream.

The pressure of HBOT drives oxygen not just into the bloodstream, but also into lymph tissue, bone tissue, red blood cells, and other critical locations. Since oxygen is critical for all healing functions, HBOT can reduce cell death, relieve pain, stimulate new growth of blood vessels, and boost circulation.

As a result, tissues damaged by radiation or suffering from nutrient deficiencies can quickly become revitalized and enhanced. The oxygenation that occurs during HBOT promotes cellular growth that combats the harmful effects of radiation therapy and helps you recover more efficiently.

Thank You

I cannot thank you enough for taking the time to read through this book. To hear my story and those of so many other incredible women whom I have connected with during this crazy ride. It's the club you never want to be part of, but once you're in, you have so many incredible women cheering you on. I pray that this book gives you the hope and courage you need! That you are inspired to take control of what you can—your mindset, your health, and your happiness.

Ask yourself: Do I want to just survive?
Or do I want to thrive?

I hope you choose to thrive. Let all the struggles that you have been through turn into something beautiful for yourself. You are so deserving and so worth it!

Peace and love, Jen

Cheers, Gratitude and All the Love

I'm not sure how I would have survived this without the incredible people in my life.

To Darren, my Mr. Worldwide, my best friend, my incredible caregiver (I think you learned from the best ;)), my everything. Thanks for being such an inspiration to me. Also, thank you for trusting me, believing in me, and holding down the fort so I could make this book, my dream, come to fruition. I love you!

To Maddie, for all the love and support from afar. I felt it! For the daily check-ins and for all the times you told me I was strong and could get through anything. You have no idea how much I needed to hear that. I love you more than you'll ever know.

To Drew, for the daily hugs. For believing in me. For being the absolute best son I could ever ask for. For hanging on the couch with me during radiation treatments, where I would be drifting in and out of sleep, watching a show by my side. When I know you probably had better things to do. I needed that! I love you more than you'll ever know.

To my mom. Thank you from the bottom of my heart for always being there for me and cheering me on. I know you would drop anything to be by my side, just as I would do for my own kids now. Thank you for teaching me that kind of love. And, of course, I can't thank you enough for all the help and input on this book. It has been so much fun and super helpful! xoxo

To my dad. My rock! Best dad I could have ever asked for. Thank you for always believing in me. It has helped so much throughout my life and in becoming the person that I am today. Just skip over the love and marriage part please ;).

To Katie Southwell, best sister I could ever ask for. Not sure where I would be without you. For making me get up and go, even though I didn't want to, but knowing full well it was exactly what I needed. Love you!

To Jenelle Summers, for being with me every moment of this crazy roller coaster. For constantly checking in on me, for listening and setting me straight when I needed it. For being the best friend I could have ever asked for. My sister from another mister—I love you!

To Chalene Johnson, for pushing me and believing that I am always capable of so much more. This would have been just a small e-book if you hadn't put that thought into my head. Whenever I'm feeling the impostor syndrome, you always set me straight. I guarantee I wouldn't be where I am today if I hadn't had your guidance. And, of course, for the styling suggestions and tips for the book cover, my graphics designer thanks you. I love you!

To my neighbors who, when I said, "No, I'm good; I don't need anything," did anyway. I'm blessed that my neighbors are also some of my closest friends. I love my village people!

To my girlfriends—you know who you are! I love each and every one of you to pieces. Thank you for the flowers and the gifts, and for stopping by with a bottle of wine so I could pretend I wasn't a cancer patient for a bit. Love you!

To my team, for supporting me during all this. The video you all did for me I'll cherish forever! And for understanding when I had to take a step back to heal. Thank you for stepping up.

To Dr. Jamie Caughran, my breast surgeon. The second I met you, I knew I was in good hands. I was a mess when I walked in and left feeling confident that I could get through this. You helped eliminate all my fears! I thank you for that! I was able to breathe again.

To Dr. Diana Bitner from True Women's Health, for keeping it real and giving me options when I didn't know I had any when it came to my hormonal health.

To Sarah Mokema, my energy healer. I can't thank you enough. When I walked in your door, I was searching for peace. And you gave me exactly that.

To Steve Durrel, my acupuncturist, thank you so much for being part of my healing team!

To the radiation crew at Lacks Cancer Center. You made one of the scariest things I've ever had to go through totally doable. Thank you for being so kind. I was actually sad to say goodbye to you all. Not so much with Roxy the Radiator (my radiation machine), though. I was ready to say goodbye to her!

To the incredible, amazing staff at Cancer and Hematology Centers of West Michigan. The staff there is top notch. Especially my oncologist, Dr. Vanderwoude; Nurse Linda, who gave me my monthly Zoladex injections; and Nurse Natalie. The treatment and care at this facility are incredible! You will feel the love. There is also an incredible nurse, Gloria, who does the blood work and typically sings patients' names when it's time for their turn.

To M. K. Meredith and Lauren Tarpley. Thank you so much for your inspiration for writing my own book and making the entire process so much easier!

To my Stronger Together Group. Thank you for being there through all the ups and downs in the beginning. And for answering all my questions. You all inspire me! Together we will continually help and inspire other women who join "the club."

To my social media friends whom I've never met in person but have felt the love. Thank you for all your support, messages, and advice on what I have gone through in the last year. It has helped immensely.

As you can see, it really does take a village.

Research – Studies – Websites – Favorites – And More

The end of this book is just the beginning. I have so much more to share! For bonus content and resources, go to www.jendelvaux.com/bookresources.

My favorite things that have helped me on my journey:

- My favorite journal: https://pushjournal.com/?rfsn=4086660.6edc3&utm_source=refersion&utm_medium=affiliate&utm_campaign=4086660.6edc3.
- For Sleep: Sleepi Gummies: https://glnk.io/z2pl/jendelvaux15
- Menopause Miracle from Pink Lotus: https://pinklotus.com/elements/?r=401.
- My favorite vegan protein powder: https://www.teambeachbody.com/shop/us/d/chocolate-plant-based-vegan-shakeology-SHKCHVegan?referringRepID=27056
- Honor Everyday Balm from: www.rosewoman.com
- My favorite water filter system, the Berkey: https://www.berkeyfilters.com/?a_aid=60b810aab9930&a_bid=91332cde.
- Tapping with Kim Salter. Her Instagram is @deignthoughtstudio _.
- Organifi Green Juice: https://glnk.io/y7z/jen. Use Code JEND for 15 percent off.

- Favorite green tea from Pique Teas: Use Code JEND for 10 percent discount: https://www.piquetea.com/?rfsn=5818415 .d1d969a&utm_source=affiliate.
- Favorite organic coffee from Foursigmatic: https://us. foursigmatic.com/?rfsn=2460080.5e3284&discount=-JENDELVAUX.
- The meditation app I use: https://www.unplug.com
- KPS Skincare: http://www.kpsessentials.com/discount/Jen10 FOR 10%

Things you can join
- My cancer group for women ready to get their health and nutrition on track. You can request to join here: https:// www.facebook.com/groups/nottodaycancerfittofight
- Bee Brave 5K: https://runsignup.com/Race/MI/Caledonia/ BeeBrave5K?remMeAttempt=.
- Not Today Cancer, Stronger Together—a super supportive, positive cancer group for women: https://www.facebook. com/groups/nottodaycancer

Not Today Cancer with Mr. Worldwide and His Bride Podcast Shows
- Episode #149. "Our Kids' Perspective on Mom and Dad Having Cancer": https://podcasts.apple.com/us/podcast/ not-today-cancer-with-mr-worldwide-and-his-bride/ id1436449587?i=1000546492170.
- Episode #127. "What's in Your Water": https://podcasts.apple.com/us/podcast/not-today-cancer-with-mr-worldwide-and-his-bride/id1436449587?i=1000529795770.
- Episode #132. "Colon Hydrotherapy—All the Ins and Outs (No Pun Intended)": https://podcasts.apple.com/us/pod-

cast/not-today-cancer-with-mr-worldwide-and-his-bride/
id1436449587?i=1000533324274.

- Episode #153. "Alcohol…Friend or foe?" https://podcasts.
  apple.com/us/podcast/not-today-cancer-with-mr-world
  wide-and-his-bride/id1436449587?i=1000547871669.

- Episode #144. "Fear of It Coming Back?" https://podcasts
  .apple.com/us/podcast/not-today-cancer-with-mr-world
  wide-and-his-bride/id1436449587?i=1000542520969.

Websites, organizations, and info from my research

Chapter two -Research on Meditation

1. UCLA
   https://connect.uclahealth.org/2021/01/29/benefits-of-
   mindfulness-meditation-for-breast-cancer-survivors/

Chapter four: Research on Journaling

1. American Society of Clinical Oncology https://ascopubs.
   org/doi/10.1200/jco.2002.08.521
2. Cancer.Net https://www.cancer.net/blog/2014-06/power-writing

Chapter six: Research on Nutrition

1. American Insitute of Cancer Research https://www.aicr.
   org/news/low-fat-diet-may-lengthen-survival-for-breast-
   cancer-survivors/
2. Mayo Clinic
   https://www.mayoclinic.org/healthy-lifestyle/nutrition-and-
   healthy-eating/in-depth/how-plant-based-food-helps-fight-
   cancer/art-20457590
3. Harvard

https://www.hsph.harvard.edu/news/press-releases/higher-dietary-fiber-intake-in-young-women-may-reduce-breast-cancer-risk/

4. Cleveland Clinic
https://health.clevelandclinic.org/vitamin-d-what-is-its-role-in-preventing-breast-cancer/

5. Dana-Farber Cancer Institute https://www.dana-farber.org/for-patients-and-families/care-and-treatment/support-services-and-amenities/nutrition-services/faqs/soy-and-cancer/

6. Cancer Therapy Advisor
https://www.cancertherapyadvisor.com/home/tools/fact-sheets/flaxseed-lignans-and-cancer/

7. Memorial Sloan Kettering Cacner Center https://www.mskcc.org/news/intermittent-fasting-and-breast-cancer-what-you-need-know

8. Webmd Cancer Center https://www.webmd.com/breast-cancer/ss/slideshow-diet-after-breast-cancer

Chapter seven: Research on Tea:
1. PubMed
https://www.ncbi.nlm.nih.gov/pmc/articles/PMC4127621/

2. Research is from the book, Cancer Hates Tea by Maria Uspenskie: www.theteaspot.com

Chapter eight - Research on Exercise
1. Mayo Clinic
https://www.mayoclinic.org/diseases-conditions/cancer/in-depth/secret-weapon-during-cancer-treatment-exercise/art-20457584

2. BreastCancer.org https://www.breastcancer.org/research-news/exercise-improves-survival-and-reduces-risk

Chapter nine - How to get back to your new normal research

1. Energy healing research from: https://www.growthwellnesstherapy.com/our-blog/5-things-everyone-needs-to-know-about-energy-healing

Chapter twelve - Going the extra mile research

1. Acupuncture research from Pub med: https://www.ncbi.nlm.nih.gov/pmc/articles/PMC2642987/
2. 10K steps a day from Dana-Farber Cancer Institute: https://www.dana-farber.org/health-library/articles/ten-thousand-steps-a-day/
3. RESEARCH FROM Pub med on melatonin: https://www.ncbi.nlm.nih.gov/pmc/articles/PMC5425818/
4. Research from The Truth about cancer on Infrared Sauna: https://thetruthaboutcancer.com/infrared-sauna-benefits/
5. Research from Food Matter on benefits of clay bath after radiation: https://www.foodmatters.com/article/bentonite-clay-a-safe-and-effective-detox-from-radiation-build-up
6. Research from UCLA Health on HBOT: https://www.uclahealth.org/hyperbaric/Workfiles/clinical_updates/hyperbaric/HyperRad-01-15-13.pdf

About the Author

Jen Delvaux is a health and fitness coach and founder of Team EmpowerNation. In February of 2021 she was diagnosed with breast cancer. She had always enjoyed researching new health hacks prior to her cancer diagnosis, but now she has made it her mission to help others take back the power over their diagnosis as well as to thrive during and after treatments.

Along with her husband, she hosts the podcast, "Not Today Cancer with Mr. Worldwide & His Bride" where they talk openly and honestly about their own struggles—Darren was diagnosed with brain cancer in 2009—and how they have been able to get through it all in a positive way.

Writing a book has always been a dream of hers. This cancer diagnosis gave her the impetus needed to share what she had learned to make an impact on the cancer community.

This book is not just for newly diagnosed women, but for women who may need a little jump start making changes in their lives to allow them to live happier, healthier lives.

CPSIA information can be obtained
at www.ICGtesting.com
Printed in the USA
LVHW070352170622
721515LV00011B/290